MODEL ANSWERS

AP BIOLOGY 2

This model answer booklet is a companion publication to provide answers for the exercises in the AP Biology 2 Student Workbook. These answers have been produced as a separate publication to keep the cost of the workbook itself to a minimum, as well as to prevent easy access to the answers by students. In most cases, simply the answer is given with no working or calculations described. A few, however, have been provided with greater detail because of their more difficult nature.

www.the**BIOZONE**.com

ISBN 978-1-927173-14-5

Copyright © 2012 Richard Allan
Published by **BIOZONE** International Ltd

PHOTOCOPYING PROHIBITED

including photocopying under a photocopy licence scheme such as CAL

Additional copies of this Model Answers book may be purchased directly from the publisher.

BIOZONE

USA, CANADA & REST OF WORLD:
BIOZONE International Ltd.
P.O. Box 13-034, Hamilton 3251, New Zealand
Telephone: +64 7-856 8104
Fax: +64 7-856 9243
Toll FREE phone: 1-866-556-2710 (USA-Canada only)
Toll FREE fax: 1 800 717 8751 (USA-Canada only)
Email: sales@biozone.co.nz
Website: www.the**BIOZONE**.com

UNITED KINGDOM & EUROPE:
BIOZONE Learning Media (UK) Ltd.
Burton upon Trent, United Kingdom
Email: sales@biozone.co.uk
Website: www.**BIOZONE**.co.uk

AUSTRALIA:
BIOZONE Learning Media Australia
Burleigh BC, QLD, Australia
Email: sales@biozone.com.au
Website: www.**BIOZONE**.com.au

Contents

Contents

Contents

Ecology

The Nature of Ecosystems

Energy Flow and Nutrient Cycles

Populations

The Diversity & Stability of Ecosystems

Entropy and Order (page 10)

1. (a) Entropy is the measure of disorder in an isolated system.
   (b) There is now a disordered state at equilibrium. All components are now thermodynamically 'equal'.

2. (a) They use energy derived from the sun or a food source to drive reactions that maintain order.
   (b) Entropy decreases by increasing the sucrose concentration inside the cell. This is done by increasing the entropy of the H^+ and the ATP. Overall entropy is increased.

Energy Inputs and Outputs (page 11)

1. **Photoautotrophs** are able to manufacture their own food from simple inorganic substances using the free energy in sunlight. **Chemoautotrophs** also manufacture their own food, but they use chemical energy to do so. The oxidation of simple inorganic molecules such as sulfide or ammonia provides the energy required to fix carbon. In contrast, **heterotrophs** cannot manufacture their own food. Their energy is obtained by consuming (feeding) on other organisms.

2. The heat comes from the process of cellular respiration.

3. Chemoautotrophs fill the primary producer role in a deep sea vent environment. They can be eaten by consumers or, if in a symbiotic relationship, the chemoautotrophs provide organic molecules which are absorbed by symbiotic hosts such as the tubeworm.

4. Although chemoautotrophic bacteria can use chemical energy to fix carbon they do this via oxidation and therefore require molecular oxygen which is provided by photosynthetic organisms on the and in the surface waters of the oceans. The animals that live off the bacteria also require oxygen for respiration.

5. (a) Waste products may contain energy rich molecules and undigested matter e.g. cellulose.
   (b) Some energy from the break down of glucose is lost as heat energy to the environment.

The Role of ATP in Cells (page 13)

1. ATP production occurs in the mitochondrion.

2. ATPase.

3. (a) ATP is required for the muscular activity involved in shivering (used to heat the body when it is cool). ATP is also required for sweating to occur (used to cool the body).
   (b) ATP hydrolysis provides the energy needed to move flagella in motile cells (e.g. a sperm cell).

4. (a) In the presence of the enzyme ATPase, ATP is hydrolyzed to produce ADP plus a free phosphate, releasing energy in the process.
   (b) Like a rechargeable battery, the ADP/ATP system toggles between a high energy and a low energy state. The addition of a phosphate to ADP recharges the molecule so that it can be used for cellular work.

5. Glucose (or pyruvate)

6. Solar energy

7. Food (plants and other animals).

8. The folded inner membrane of a mitochondrion greatly increases the surface area. This allows more ATPase molecules to occupy membrane and increases the ability to produce ATP.

9. Highly active cells require a lot of energy (ATP) to move. Therefore, they have large numbers of mitochondria so that enough ATP can be produced to meet their energy demands.

10. (a) More energy is required.
    (b) It is not possible to get more energy out than you have put in, therefore, the regeneration of ATP will cost more than 30.7 kJ.

Energy Transformation in Cells (page 15)

1. Heterotrophs (strictly chemoheterotrophs) derive energy for biosynthesis from an organic energy source (other living organisms, their dead remains, or their excreted/egested products). Photosynthetic autotrophs (photoautotrophs) derive energy for biosynthesis from light energy (e.g. sunlight, which is the inorganic energy source). Chemosynthetic autotrophs (chemoautotrophs) derive energy for biosynthesis from an inorganic chemical energy source (e.g. hydrogen sulfide gas from volcanic vents).

2. (a) At this depth there is no sunlight (it is filtered out after several hundred metres). Photosynthetic organisms require a source of sunlight.
   (b) Hydrogen sulfide.
   (c) They would die due to inability to respire.
   (d) Chemosynthetic autotrophs (chemoautotrophs).

ATP Production in Cells (page 16)

1. (a) Glycolysis: cytoplasm
   (b) Krebs cycle: matrix of mitochondria
   (c) Electron transport chain: cristae (inner membrane surface) of mitochondria.

2. The ATP generated in glycolysis and the Krebs cycle is generated by substrate level phosphorylation, i.e. transfer of a phosphate group directly from a substrate to ADP. In contrast, the ATP generated via the electron transport chain is through oxidative phosphorylation, a step-wise series of reduction-oxidation reactions that provide the energy for forming ATP. Oxidative phosphorylation yields much more ATP per glucose than substrate level phosphorylation.

The Biochemistry of Respiration (page 17)

1. (a) The breakdown of glucose (a 6-C sugar) into two molecules of pyruvate (a 3-C acid) in the cytoplasm. The process is anaerobic and generates a net two molecules of ATP.
   (b) When oxygen is present, pyruvate enters the matrix of the mitochondria and CO_2 is removed. Coenzyme A (CoA) picks up the remaining 2-C fragment of pyruvate to form acetyl coenzyme A.
   (c) The acetyl group passes into a cyclic reaction (also in the matrix) combining a 4-C molecule into a 6-C molecule and releasing the CoA for reuse. CO_2 is removed and two molecules of ATP are made.
   (d) Comprises a series of reactions involving H^+ and e- along the membranes of the cristae in the mitochondria. H^+ and e- lose energy along the chain which is used to produce ATP molecules.

2. For maximum theoretical yield:
   (a) Glycolysis: 2 ATPs
   (b) Krebs cycle: 2 ATPs
   (c) Electron transport chain: 34 ATPs
   (d) Total produced: 38 ATPs

3. Released as carbon dioxide gas and breathed out through gas exchange surfaces.

4. (a) Hydrogen atoms supply energy in the form of high energy electrons. These are passed along the electron transport chain, losing energy as they go which is used to generate ATP.
   (b) NAD and FAD are hydrogen acceptors, transporting hydrogens to the electron transport chain.
   (c) Oxygen is the final electron acceptor at the end of the electron transport chain.
   (d) Acetyl coenzyme A, formed from pyruvate in the transition reaction, enters the Krebs cycle where CoA is released and recycled.

5. When glucose is limiting for aerobic respiration, other organic molecules e.g. fats and ultimately even protein, can provide alternative respiratory substrates.

Chemiosmosis (page 19)

1. In chemiosmosis, ATP synthesis is coupled to electron transport and movement of hydrogen ions. Energy from the passage of electrons along the chain of electron carriers is used to pump protons (H^+), against their concentration gradient, into the intermembrane space, creating a high concentration of protons there. The protons return across the membrane down a concentration gradient via the enzyme complex, ATP synthase, which synthesizes the ATP.

2. Elevating the proton concentration outside the exposed inner mitochondrial membranes would result in their flowing down their concentration gradient via ATP synthase and generating ATP.

3. A suspension of isolated chloroplasts would become alkaline because protons would be removed from the medium as ATP was generated.

4. (a) By placing chloroplasts in an acid medium, the thylakoid interior was acidified. Transfer to an alkaline medium established a proton gradient from the thylakoid interior to the medium.
   (b) The protons could flow down the concentration gradient established, via ATP synthase, and generate ATP.

Anaerobic Pathways for ATP Production (page 20)

1. **Aerobic respiration** requires the presence of oxygen and produces a lot of useable energy (ATP). **Fermentation** does not require oxygen and uses an alternative H^+ acceptor. There is little useable energy produced (the only ATP generated is via glycolysis).

2. (a) $2 \div 38 \times 100 = 5.3\%$ efficiency
   (b) Only a small amount of the energy of a glucose molecule is released in anaerobic respiration. The remainder stays locked up in the molecule.

3. The build up of toxic products (ethanol or lactate)

inhibits further metabolic activity.

Investigating Yeast Fermentation (page 21)

1. $C_6H_{12}O_6 \rightarrow C_2H_5OH + 2CO_2$

2. Calculated rate of CO_2 production, group 1:
   (a) None: 0 $cm^3\,min^{-1}$ or 0 $cm^3\,s^{-1}$
   (b) Glucose: 0.443 $cm^3\,min^{-1}$ or 7.4 x 10^{-3} $cm^3\,s^{-1}$
   (c) Maltose: 0.24 $cm^3\,min^{-1}$ or 4.0 x 10^{-3} $cm^3\,s^{-1}$
   (d) Sucrose: 0.191 $cm^3\,min^{-1}$ or 3.2 x 10^{-3} $cm^3\,s^{-1}$
   (e) Lactose: 0.029 $cm^3\,min^{-1}$ or 4.8 x 10^{-4} $cm^3\,s^{-1}$

3. Calculated rate of CO_2 production, group 2:
   (a) None: 0 $cm^3\,min^{-1}$ or 0 cm^3s^{-1}
   (b) Glucose: 0.271 $cm^3\,min^{-1}$ or 4.5 x 10^{-3} $cm^3\,s^{-1}$
   (c) Maltose: 0.211 $cm^3\,min^{-1}$ or 3.5 x 10^{-3} $cm^3\,s^{-1}$
   (d) Sucrose: 0.194 $cm^3\,min^{-1}$ or 3.2 x 10^{-3} $cm^3\,s^{-1}$
   (e) Lactose: 0 $cm^3\,min^{-1}$ or 0 $cm^3\,s^{-1}$

4. The assumptions made are that 24°C and pH 4.5 provide suitable (even optimal) conditions for yeast fermentation. This is reasonable as it has been stated in the background that the literature cites warm, slightly acidic conditions as optimal for baker's yeast.

5. Graph of Group 1's results: see top of next page.

6. (a) The fermentation rates were greatest for the substrate glucose, with a CO_2 yield approximately twice that for maltose and sucrose. Maltose and sucrose were similar to each other, while the rate of fermentation on lactose was minimal.
   (b) Glucose is the preferred substrate (directly available as a fuel). Maltose (glucose-glucose) and sucrose (glucose-fructose) must first be hydrolyzed before the glucose is available (the fructose from sucrose must also be isomerized to glucose). This accounts for the lower fermentation rates on these substrates. Lactose is a poor fuel, presumably because yeast lack the enzyme to hydrolyze the galactose and glucose that form this disaccharide.

7. (a) Column chart comparing results of the two groups.

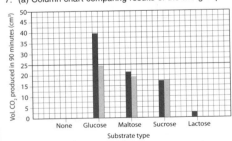

Chloroplasts (page 23)

1. (a) Stroma
   (b) Stroma lamellae
   (c) Outer membrane
   (d) Granum
   (e) Thylakoid
   (f) Inner membrane

2. (a) Chlorophyll is found in the thylakoid membrane.
   (b) Chlorophyll is a membrane-bound pigment found in and around the photosystems that embedded in the membranes. Light capture by chlorophyll is linked to electron transport in the light dependent reactions.

Cumulative volume of CO_2 produced over 90 minutes by yeast grown on different carbohydrate sources.

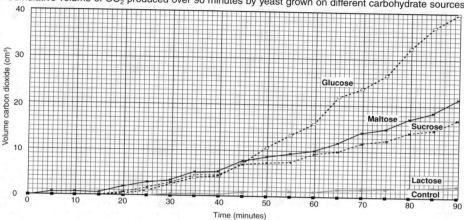

3. The internal membranes provide a large surface area for binding chlorophyll molecules and capturing light. Membranes are stacked in such a way that they do not shade each other.

4. Chlorophyll absorbs blue and red light but reflects green light, so leaves look green to the human eye.

Photosynthesis (page 24)
1. Importance of photosynthesis (in any order):
   (a) Transforms light energy into chemical energy available to food chains.
   (b) Creates organic molecules used as building blocks for creating more complex molecules.
   (c) Releases free oxygen into the atmosphere; oxygen is required by many other life forms.

2. (a) **NADP**: Carries H_2 from the light dependent phase to the light independent reactions.
   (b) **ATP**: Provides energy for constructing glucose molecules using hydrogens (delivered by NADP) and carbon dioxide.
   (c) **Chlorophyll**: Absorbs the light energy for photosynthesis, producing high energy electrons. These are used to make ATP and NADPH. The photosystems (of which chlorophylls are a part) also split water molecules, to release H^+ (for use in the light independent reactions) and liberate free O_2.
   (d) **Light**: Provides the ultimate energy source to drive the light dependent reactions (creation of ATP and reduced NADP).

Chloroplasts (page 23)
1. The absorption spectrum of a pigment is that wavelength of the light spectrum absorbed by a pigment, e.g. chlorophyll absorbs red and blue light and appears green. Represented graphically, the absorption spectrum shows the relative amounts of light absorbed at different wavelengths.

2. Accessory pigments absorb light wavelengths that chlorophyll a cannot absorb, and they pass their energy on to chlorophyll a. This broadens the action spectrum

over which chlorophyll a can fuel photosynthesis.

Light Dependent Reactions (page 26)
1. **NADP**: Carries H_2 from the light dependent phase to the light independent reactions.

2. **Chlorophyll**: These pigment molecules trap light energy and produce high energy electrons. These are used to make ATP and NADPH. The chlorophyll molecules also split water, releasing H^+ for use in the light independent reactions and liberating free O_2.

3. Light dependent (D) phase takes place in the grana (thylakoid membranes) of the chloroplast and requires light energy to proceed. The light dependent phase generates ATP and reducing power in the form of NADPH. The electrons and hydrogen ions come from the splitting of water.

4. The ATP synthesis is coupled to electron transport. When the light strikes the chlorophyll molecules, high energy electrons are released by the chlorophyll molecules. The energy lost when the electrons are passed through a series of electron carriers is used to bond a phosphate to ADP to make ATP.
   Note: ATP is generated (in photosynthesis and cellular respiration) by **chemiosmosis**. As the electron carriers pick up the electrons, protons (H^+) pass into the space inside the thylakoid, creating a high concentration of protons there. The protons return across the thylakoid membrane down a concentration gradient via the enzyme complex, ATP synthetase that synthesizes the ATP (also called ATP synthase or ATPase).

5. (a) **Non-cyclic (photo)phosphorylation**: Generation of ATP using light energy during photosynthesis. The electrons lost during this process are replaced by the splitting of water.
   (b) The term non-cyclic **photo**phosphorylation is also (commonly) used because it indicates that the energy for the phosphorylation is coming from light.

6. (a) In **cyclic photophosphorylation**, the electrons lost from photosystem II are replaced by those from photosystem I rather than from the splitting

of water. ATP is generated in this process, but not NADPH. **Note**: In the cell, both cyclic and non-cyclic photophosphorylation operate to different degrees to balance production of NADPH and ATP.

(b) The non-cyclic path produces ATP and NADH in roughly equal quantities but the Calvin cycle uses more ATP than NADPH. The cyclic pathway of electron flow makes up the difference.

7. It shows that a complex reaction pathway is made of less complex pathways that can operate independently. These simple pathways can then be linked through common intermediates, generating complex pathways.

Light Independent Reactions (page 28)

1. (a) 6   (b) 6   (c) 12
   (d) 12   (e) 12   (f) 6
   (g) 2   (h) 1

2. RuBisCo catalyses the reaction that splits CO_2 and joins it with ribulose 1,5-bisphosphate. It fixes carbon from the atmosphere.

3. Triose phosphate (note that you may also see this referred to as glyceraldehyde-3-phosphate, GALP, G3P or PGAL)

4. $6CO_2 + 18ATP + 12$ NADPH $+ 12H^+$
   $\rightarrow 1$ glucose $+18ADP + 18P_i +12$ NADP$^+ + 6H_2O$

5. The Calvin cycle will cease in the dark in most plants because the light dependent reactions stop, therefore no NADPH or ATP is produced. At night, stomata also close, reducing levels of CO_2 (there will still be some CO_2 in the leaf as a waste product of respiration).

KEY TERMS: Crossword (page 29)

Answers Across
1. Chemiosmosis
5. Chloroplast
8. Heterotroph
9. Autotroph
13. Electron transport chain
15. Glycolysis
16. Producer
17. Dependent

Answers Down
1. Cellular respiration
2. Mitochondrion
3. Photosynthesis
4. Entropy
5. Consumer
6. Chlorophyll
7. Fermentation
10. Krebs cycle
11. Anaerobic
12. Independent
14. ATP

Enzymes (page 31)

1. The active site is the region where substrate is drawn in and positioned in such a way as to promote the reaction. The properties of the active site are a function of the precise configuration of the amino acid side chains which interact with the substrate.

2. A mutation could result in a different amino acid being positioned in the polypeptide chain. The final protein may be folded incorrectly (incorrect tertiary and quaternary structure) and lose its biological function. **Note**: If the mutation is silent or in a non-critical region of the enzyme, biological function may not be affected.

3. **Catabolism** involves metabolic reactions that break large molecules into smaller ones. Such reactions include digestion and cellular respiration. They release energy and are therefore **exergonic**. In contrast, **anabolism** involves metabolic reactions that build larger molecules from smaller ones. Anabolic reactions include protein synthesis and photosynthesis. They require the input of energy and are **endergonic**.

How Enzymes Work (page 31)

1. Enzymes are biological molecules (usually proteins) that act as catalysts, allowing reactions to proceed more readily. They do this by influencing bond stability in the reactants and thereby lowering the activation energy required to create an unstable transition state in the substrate from which the reaction proceeds readily.

2. The **lock and key model** proposed that the substrate was simply drawn into a closely matching cleft (active site) on the enzyme. In this model, the enzyme's active site was a somewhat passive recipient of the substrate, whereas studies of enzyme inhibitors since showed that assumption to be incorrect.

3. The **induced fit model** is a modified version of the lock and key in which the substrate and the active site interact. Substrate binding causes the active site to change slightly so that bonds in the substrate(s) are destabilized. This model is supported by evidence from studies of enzyme inhibition.

Enzyme Reaction Rates (page 33)

1. (a) Increased enzyme concentration increases the reaction rate.
   (b) A cell may vary the amount of enzyme present by manufacturing more (increasing rate of synthesis).

2. (a) An increase in substrate concentration increases reaction rate to a point. Reaction rate does not continue increasing but levels off as the amount of substrate continues to increase.
   (b) The rate changes (levels off) because after a certain substrate level the enzymes are saturated by the substrate and the reaction rate cannot increase.

3. (a) An optimum temperature for an enzyme is the temperature where enzyme activity is maximal.
   (b) Most enzymes perform poorly at low temperatures because chemical reactions occur slowly or not at all at low temperatures (enzyme activity will reappear when the temperature increases; usually enzymes are not damaged by low temperatures).

4. (a) Optimum pH: pepsin: 1-2, trypsin: approx. 7.5-8.2, urease: approx. 6.5-7.0.
   (b) The stomach is an acidic environment which is the ideal pH for pepsin.

Enzyme Cofactors (page 34)

1. **Cofactors** are non-protein components that complete an enzyme, i.e. enable its functional catalytic activity.

2. Cofactors either complete the active site or make the active site more reactive (e.g. by facilitating the substrate-enzyme interaction).

3. The apoenzyme is the protein portion of the functionally active enzyme. The cofactor is the non-protein portion required to complete the enzyme's catalytic activity.

4. Two broad categories of cofactors are **organic cofactors**, such as vitamin C, and **inorganic ions**

(such as Ca^{2+} and Zn^{2+}).

5. Many vitamins and minerals are cofactors so an adequate dietary intake ensures that all necessary cofactors are present as required for enzyme function.

Enzyme Inhibitors (page 35)

1. In **competitive inhibition**, the inhibitor competes with the substrate for the enzyme's active site and, once in place, prevents substrate binding. A **noncompetitive inhibitor** does not occupy the active site but binds to some other part of the enzyme, making it less able to perform its function as an effective biological catalyst.

2. (a) With a competitive inhibitor present, the effect of the competition can be overcome by increasing the substrate concentration; the rate of the reaction will slow, but will eventually reach the same level as that achieved without an inhibitor. In a system where there is a non-competitive inhibitor, the rate of the reaction slows and is well below the maximum that can be achieved without an inhibitor. This rate depression cannot be overcome by increasing the substrate concentration.
   (b) Type of inhibition could be tested by increasing the substrate concentration. If this overcame the rate depression then the inhibition is competitive.

3. Allosteric regulators bind to an allosteric site (not the active site) on an enzyme changing the shape of the active site. Depending on the type of regulator that binds, the enzyme may be activated or inactivated.

4. Heavy metals are toxic because they permanently stop enzyme activity, rendering the enzyme non-functional usually, but not exclusively, through non-competitive inhibition. Because they are lost exceedingly slowly from the body, anything other than a low level of these metals is toxic.

5. (a) Some antibiotics, such as penicillin, are irreversible inhibitors to the enzymes essential for wall synthesis in bacteria. Susceptible bacteria are unable to build cell walls after dividing so their growth is stopped.
   (b) Human cells do not have a cell wall and so they are unaffected by the enzyme inhibition.

Catalase Activity in Germinating Seeds

(page 37)

1. $2H_2O_2 \rightarrow 2H_2O + O_2$

2. (a)-(c), completed table for mean, standard deviation, and rate below.

Stage	Mean	Std dev	Mean rate (cm^3 s^{-1} g^{-1})
0.5	10.1	0.5	0.03
2	34.9	3.8	0.12
4	65.5	5.0	0.22
6	36.7	4.0	0.12
10	22.5	2.7	0.08

3. (a) The values obtained for the 0.5 days and 10 days of germination are not in accordance with those obtained by the other groups (trials). The other values are of a similar magnitude.
   (b) If the new data are used, the mean should exclude

those two values and be calculated using only 5 (rather than 6) trials for those germination stages.
   (c) These data values are clearly well adrift from the other values obtained for those stages from other groups (trial); if plotted as a scatter plot, they are distinct outliers on the plot. This suggests that something was wrong with either the measurement or the execution of the trial. It is reasonable therefore to exclude them from the analysis.

4.

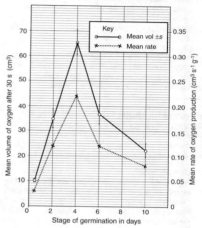

Catalase activity in relation to stage of germination in mung bean seedlings

5. (a) The volume and rate of oxygen production increases rapidly to a peak at 4 days and declines, almost as sharply between 4 and 10 days.
   (b) Catalase activity in the sprouting seeds increases rapidly in the first 4 days of germination linked to the increase in cell activity and high respiration rates in early growth. It then falls off as the seedlings become established and metabolism slows. ~~Either statement~~ Both statements

6. Errors include: The equipment could potentially leak around the bung or the tubing. There could be a delay in delivering all the H_2O_2 so a slight delay in correctly timing the start of the reaction. The seeds might not be completely crushed, or crushed to different degrees so that not all the catalase is released.

7. Validity of data could be affected by (two of): insufficient usable data, very variable data (overlapping data between times), old or poorly stored beans, old or poorly stored H_2O_2, precise and reliable data which was inaccurate because of gas losses through the equipment.

8. Improvements could include any one of: Using a mechanical grinder for a set period of time to ensure complete release of catalase. Using a petroleum sealant to prevent air leaks. Making sure the same person takes the measurement in each case, making sure all the trials are carried out with the same equipment by the same team.

Levels of Organization (page 39)

1. **Animals**
   (a) **Molecular**: Adrenaline, collagen, DNA, phospholipid
   (b) **Organelles**: Lysosome, ribosomes
   (c) **Cells**: Leukocyte, mast cell, neuron, Schwann cell
   (d) **Tissues**: Blood, bone, cardiac muscle, cartilage, squamous epithelium
   (e) **Organs**: Brain, heart, spleen
   (f) **Organ system**: Nervous system, reproductive system

2. **Plants**
   (a) **Molecular**: Pectin, cellulose, DNA, phospholipid
   (b) **Organelles**: Chloroplasts, ribosomes
   (c) **Cells**: Companion cells, epidermal cell, fibers, tracheid
   (d) **Tissues**: Collenchyma*, mesophyll, parenchyma*, phloem, sclerenchyma
   (e) **Organs**: Flowers, leaf, roots
   * **Note**: Parenchyma and collenchyma are simple tissues comprising only one type of cell (parenchyma and collenchyma cells respectively). Simple plant tissues are usually identified by cell name alone.

Achieving Metabolic Efficiency (page 40)

1. Metabolic efficiency refers to how cells produce the products they need to carry out cell processes in the most energy efficient way. This prevents excess energy being wasted.

2. (a) **Compartmentalization**: Regions of some organelles (e.g. mitochondrion) are separated by membranes into different areas. This allows certain metabolic reactions, and the enzymes required for that reaction to occur, to be isolated in a specific region. All of the required components are in one place, increasing efficiency.
   (b) **Feedback inhibition**: The build up of the end product of a metabolic pathway (or in some cases, build up of intermediate products), inhibits (stops) the enzymes from working. This prevents the cell from making products unnecessarily, and so conserves energy (increases metabolic efficiency).

3. Cells would expend energy producing products that they did not need. This may leave them with not enough energy or resources to produce what they require.

Regional Specialization and Functional Efficiency (page 41)

1. (a) Organ specialization allows an organ to perform a particular task (or set of related tasks) more efficiently than if it had to carry out a range of different tasks. It saves energy.
   (b) In multicellular organisms, functional efficiency can be achieved by having specific cells, organs (or organ systems) dedicated to carrying out a particular role, or series of related roles.

2. In mammals, regional functionality of the digestive system is achieved by having food move in one direction through the digestive system. This allows regions of the digestive system to have specialized roles in the digestion of food (e.g. the highly acidic stomach allows pepsin to begin to breakdown proteins, and the small intestine is very long and has a large surface area to maximize absorption).

Metabolism in Bacterial Communities (page 42)

1. (a) Biofilms are formed when microbial communities attach to structures in an organized manner.
   (b) Formation of a biofilm changes the metabolism of the microbial community in such a way that new properties may emerge (e.g. antibiotic resistance). It also offers protection from the environment (e.g. from drying out) and optimizes resource use.
   (c) Understanding how biofilms form can help researchers to devise ways to prevent their formation or remove them once the have formed in undesirable situations (e.g. removal of dental plaques, or the prevention of biofilm formation in industrial heat exchangers).

2. Any of:
   – *Myxococcus xanthus* forms spherical colonies trapping cyanobacteria inside, so the colony can feed on an energy-efficient way *en masse*.
   – Cyanobacteria, such as *Anabaena*, form long photosynthetic chains. When nitrogen levels are low, some cells differentiate into heterocysts, and are able to fix nitrogen. Nitrogen is shared with neighboring *Anabaena* cells, an in return they are given nutrients.
   – A marine bacterium, *Thiovulum*, forms swarms at the transition zone between oxygen rich water and sulfide rich water above thermal vents. By swimming as a group, the mesh community can move to control the amount of oxygen or sulfide they receive.

KEY TERMS: Crossword (page 43)

Answers Across
2. Catalyst
6. Catabolism
7. Metabolic pathway
9. Allosteric regulation
10. Competitive
12. Inhibition
13. Endergonic
14. Exergonic
15. Biofilm
16. Enzyme

Answers Down
1. Optimum
2. Cofactor
3. Denaturation
4. Activation energy
5. Anabolism
8. Active site
11. Coenzyme

Metabolism and Body Size (page 45)

1. (a) Graph plotted using *Excel*®

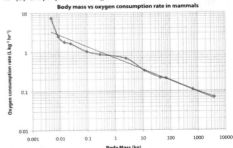

Body mass vs oxygen consumption rate in mammals

   (b) The graph is a straight line, with a linear relationship between body mass and oxygen consumption.

2. The shrew has a faster metabolic rate than a large mammal. As a result, it uses more energy per gram of

body weight, so needs to eat relatively more food, more often to meet its metabolic requirements.

3. (a) $650^{-.25}$ x 70 = 13.8, $0.005^{-.25}$ x 70 = 263
   263 ÷ 13.8 = 19
   (b) $70^{-.25}$ x 70 = 24.2, $0.29^{-.25}$ x 70 = 95.4
   95.4 ÷ 24.2 = 3.9

4. An organism with a high metabolic rate cannot dive for as long as an organism with a lower metabolic rate because it uses oxygen at a faster rate.

How Organisms Allocate Energy (page 46)

1. Organisms must carefully gauge how much energy they will expend obtaining food because if the energy expended exceeds the energy obtained, the organism will suffer a net energy loss (and starve).

2. (a) Animals migrate to areas where resources (such as food and water) are plentiful. The energy obtained from these resources is enough to allow the animals to breed and rear young, and provides sufficient energy for the return migration.
   (b) Hibernation occurs during periods of low food supply (usually winter at higher latitudes). During hibernation an animal significantly reduces its metabolic rate, enabling it to survive without feeding. Without hibernation, animals would probably starve because their energy losses would exceed energy gains from foraging.

3. (a) Graph plotted using *Excel*®

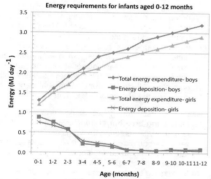

Energy requirements for infants aged 0-12 months

(b) Energy expenditure increases sharply for the first 4-5 months of life. After 5 months, energy expenditure still increases, but not as sharply.
(c) Energy deposition is very rapid for the first 3-4 months of life, and then begins to drop off.
(d) It is high (35%) at birth, and then drops to 3%.

4. Excess energy is stored as fat.

Energy and Seasonal Breeding (page 48)

1. An annual reproductive cycle is associated with favorable conditions for breeding (high resource availability, favorable temperatures). At other times of the year, breeding would be too costly in terms of energy expenditure.

2. (a) Males spend most of their energy in courtship (attracting a mate), fending off rival males for mating rights or in defense of territory and in mating itself.
   (b) Females expend most of their energy in maintaining their pregnancy and in rearing their young.

3. Raising young often coincides with Spring because this is when food resources are most abundant. It also maximizes the time available for growth and rearing of the young before winter, giving the young the best possible chance for surviving the winter.

Reproductive Allocation and Parental Care (page 49)

1. Availability of adequate resources to support young to independence is a major factor determining whether or not animals will reproduce.

2. Animals show two broad types of strategy for parental care: little or no energy investment in care of the offspring (e.g. mollusks), and substantial parental care (e.g. mammals). Animals with little or no parental care produce very large numbers of young or eggs enhancing the chances that a few will survive to reproductive age themselves. Most of the reproductive effort is directed at the production of the young. In contrast, animals with high levels of parental care (e.g. birds and mammals) produce very few eggs or offspring. A large proportion of the reproductive effort is invested in caring for the smaller number of offspring to ensure that they survive to reproductive age. In reality, the parental care strategies of animals represent a continuum between these two extremes.

Diapause as a Reproductive Strategy (page 50)

1. (a) Offspring number 3 died at heel.
   (b) Offspring 4 and 5 were in the pouch when they died.
   (c) Two young were in progress during the period of temporary improvement. No. 6 was in the pouch and no. 7 was in diapause in the uterus.
   (d) Required answers in bold: During the drought the following events occurred:
      (i) **Offspring 6** (joey at heel) **died** and **offspring 7** completed embryonic development and **moved into the pouch**.
      (ii) Offspring 7 died soon after entering the pouch and **offspring 8 came out of diapause** and finished its embryonic development.
      (iii) **Offspring 8 entered the pouch**.
      (iv) **Offspring 8 died**, still in the pouch. The female ceased to reproduce (did not enter estrous).
   (e) After the drought broke, the embryonic diapause stage was missed out because there were no other young in the pouch and the female allowed the embryonic fertilization to proceed directly after estrous and fertilization.

2. Required answer in bold: **Offspring die in descending order of maternal energy drain (greatest to least).** The joey at heel represents the largest energy drain on the mother and is cut off from the milk supply first so other, less energy-demanding young have a chance to survive. If conditions deteriorate further, then the pouch young die. The diapausing embryo is a small energy drain on the mother and is the last to die.

Negative Feedback (page 51)

1. **Receptors** (detect stimuli), **control and coordination centre** (integration of signals and coordination of response), **effectors** (implement appropriate response).

2. Negative feedback mechanisms are self-correcting (the response acts to oppose changes to the input) so that fluctuations are dampened. This stabilizes physiological systems against excessive change and enables maintenance of a steady state.

Positive Feedback (page 52)

1. (a) Positive feedback has a role in accelerating a physiological process to bring about a particular required response. Examples include (1) elevation in body temperature (fever) to accelerate protective immune responses, (2) positive feedback between estrogen and LH to leading to an LH surge and ovulation, (3) positive feedback between oxytocin and uterine contractions: oxytocin causes uterine contraction and stretching of the cervix, which causes more release of oxytocin and so on until the delivery of the infant, (4) positive feedback in fruit ripening where ethylene accelerates ripening of nearby fruit.

   (b) Positive feedback is inherently unstable because it causes an escalation in the physiological response, pushing it outside the tolerable physiological range. Compare this with negative feedback, which is self correcting and causes the system to return to the steady state.

   (c) Positive feedback loops are normally ended by a resolution of situation causing the initial stimulation. For example, the positive feedback loop between estrogen and LH leading to ovulation is initiated by high estrogen levels and ended when these fall quickly after ovulation, prompting a resumption of negative feedback mechanisms. In childbirth, once the infant is delivered, the stretching of the cervix ceases and so too does the stimulation for more oxytocin release.

   (d) When positive feedback continues unchecked, it can lead to physiological collapse. One example includes unresolved fever. If an infection is not brought under control (e.g. by the body's immune system mechanisms or medical intervention), body temperature will continue to rise and can lead to seizures, neurological damage, and death.

Maintaining Homeostasis (page 53)

1. Two mechanisms operating to restore homeostasis after infection ((a) and (b) any two of):
   - Immune system response with the production of antibodies against the antigens of the pathogen (humoral response).
   - Immune system response with the production of T cells which recognize the antigens of the pathogen and destroy them directly (cell-mediated response).
   - Local inflammatory response (redness, pain, swelling, heat) at the site of infection.
   - Fever (widespread increase in body temperature).
   - The production of antimicrobial substances like interferon and interleukin-1.
   - Phagocytosis of pathogen by white blood cells.
   All the above aim to destroy the pathogen and/or its toxins and assist a return to homeostasis.

For Q. 2-4, more explanatory detail than required is given.

2. Mechanisms by which responses to stimuli are brought about and coordinated:

   (a) **Hormonal response** to stimuli: Endocrine glands respond to a stimulus (e.g. a nerve impulse or another hormone or metabolite) by producing hormones which bring about an appropriate physiological response. **For example**, nervous stimulation of the adrenal glands when the body receives a stressful stimulus causes the release of adrenalin. This hormone causes mobilization of glucose in muscle and liver cells, increases heart rate and directs blood away from nonessential organs. These responses help the body react to the stress situation.

   (b) **Nervous response** to stimuli: Direct stimulation of nerves from a sensory receptor causes a reaction to the stimulus. This may be a response requiring interpretation of the message by the brain or it may be a reflex (an automatic response to a stimulus involving only 2 or 3 neurons), e.g. pain withdrawal.

3. Maintaining water and ion balance by:

   (a) Water and ions are taken in with food and drink, helping to replace that lost through urine, feces, and sweat. The digestive organs and all of the digestive hormones (e.g. amylase in the mouth, pepsin in the stomach, trypsin in the small intestine) are all involved in breaking down food and facilitating absorption into the bloodstream.

   (b) The kidney is the primary regulator of fluid and ions. When large quantities of fluid must be excreted, the kidney produces large amounts of dilute urine. When water must be conserved, small amounts of concentrated urine are produced. ADH (antidiuretic hormone) causes more water to be reabsorbed from the kidney (causing a more concentrated urine). ADH increases when blood water levels are low. Essential ions (and glucose) are retained by active reabsorption from the kidney tubules. Another hormone, aldosterone from the adrenal glands, increases the absorption of sodium ions.

4. Regulating respiratory gases during exercise by:

   (a) **Increasing breathing rate.** This increases both the rate of oxygen entering the lungs and the rate at which carbon dioxide leaves. It also increases the rate of loading and unloading of oxygen and carbon dioxide into and out of the bloodstream.

   (b) **Increasing the heart rate.** This increases blood flow which facilitates the loading and unloading of oxygen and carbon dioxide into and out of the bloodstream. It also increases the speed of delivery of oxygen to working tissues (e.g. muscles) and speeds up the removal of carbon dioxide and other waste products of metabolism.

Mechanisms of Thermoregulation (page 55)

1. (a) A **homeothermic endotherm** maintains a constant (usually high) body temperature despite environmental fluctuations. It does this using internal sources of energy (metabolic activity).

   (b) Many terrestrial lizards and snakes regulate their body temperature to within quite narrow limits using behavioral mechanisms. Their body temperature does not simply fluctuate with ambient temperature.

2. (a) Letting body temperature fluctuate with the environment saves a great deal of energy because the animal does not have to maintain body temperature against environmental variation.

(b) Ectothermy represents an energy saving since ectotherms are not physiologically committed to maintaining a high metabolic rate. Lower metabolic rates are advantageous when food supplies are low (less energy is required to sustain the animal).

3. Endotherms that undergo torpor usually do so when food supplies are scarce and/or when the metabolic cost of maintaining activity is likely to be prohibitively high (e.g. during very cold weather). Lowering metabolic rates at these times saves energy and allows them to survive until conditions are more favorable.

4. (a) Ectotherm's body temperature increases steadily with increasing ambient temperature. Endotherms maintain a high, constant body temperature despite changes in the environmental temperature.

(b) An poikilothermic ectotherm would be restricted to temperatures below about 40-45°C because above this point its body temperature would continue to rise to a state of physiological heat stress.

(c) Optimum temperature range for an endotherm is from 18° or 19°C to 36°C. Between these temperatures, oxygen consumption, and therefore energy expenditure, is lowest.

(d) At temperatures below 15°C the energetic costs of thermoregulation for an endotherm increase markedly because the environmental temperature is low compared with the preferred constant body temperature and more energy is required to maintain body temperature against heat loss. At temperatures above 35°C the energetic costs of thermoregulation also increase because large amounts of energy begin to be used to dissipate excess heat and prevent further heat gain.

(e) For ectotherms, the energetic costs of temperature regulation increase steadily with the environmental temperature because as the environmental temperature increases so too does the metabolic rate of the animal. Increased metabolic rate equates to increased energetic expenditure and higher oxygen consumption.

Thermoregulation in Animals (page 57)

1. (a) Water transmits heat away from the body very rapidly, therefore it has a great cooling capacity.

(b) Any two of: • Countercurrent heat exchange systems in fins and flippers • Insulated body surfaces of thick fat • Large body size.

(c) Large body size reduces the surface area (compared to volume) over which heat can be lost.

(d) Any of: High heat production through high metabolic rate, consumption of large amounts of food, hibernation or torpor during winter periods.

2. (a) Thick hair reduces heat loss by trapping an insulating layer of air between the animal and the cooler environment. The insulating layer of hair also reduces heat gain from the environment.

(b) Different fur thicknesses allow an animal to expose or cover thinner areas to allow for greater of lower heat loss depending on needs.

(c) Related species at low altitude could be expected to have less thick and less dense fur covering than

animals at high altitude.

(d) They have a thick layer of fat (blubber) underneath the skin. In addition, they are usually large.

3. **Countercurrent heat exchanges** provide a physiological mechanism by which heat transfers between arterial and venous blood maintain the blood entering vital organs of the body at a relatively constant temperature. In the flukes and fins of marine mammals, arterial blood cools as it enters the limb, warming the blood that is returning to the body. In some desert ungulates, the countercurrent exchange operates so that cooler venous blood, returning to the body from the facial regions, lowers the temperature to the arterial blood before it supplies the brain.

4. (a) Animals may group together to retain body heat. By creating a large single mass, heat loss is reduced. Examples include many livestock species (sheep and cattle), many rodents, penguins, honeybees.

(b) Any of the following behaviors:
For mammals living in cold regions, e.g. Arctic fox, huddling in a burrow or scrape so that minimal surface area is exposed to temperature loss.
For larger animals in hot regions, e.g. kangaroos, licking the fur (particularly areas well supplied with blood) to increase evaporative cooling. Some mammals also take up postures to maximize heat loss (e.g. exposing areas of thinner fur to increase the area over which heat can be lost).
For small, desert dwelling mammals, nocturnal behavior (i.e. avoidance of daytime temperatures) is important in thermoregulation.

Thermoregulation in Humans (page 59)

1. Body temperature reduced by ((a) and (b) any two of):
• Sweating (cooling by evaporation) • Reducing activity
• Behavioral mechanisms such as removing clothing or seeking shade • Increasing blood flow to skin (leads to increased radiation from the skin surface) .

2. (a) **Hypothalamus**: Monitors temperature changes in the body and coordinates appropriate responses to counteract the changes.

(b) **Skin**: Detects changes in skin temperature and relays the information to the hypothalamus. In response to input from the hypothalamus, muscles and capillaries in the skin act as effectors to bring about an appropriate thermoregulatory response.

(c) **Nervous input to effectors** (from hypothalamus): Brings about (through stimulation of muscles) an appropriate thermoregulatory response (e.g. raising hairs, constricting blood vessels).

(d) **Hormones**: Mediate a change in metabolic rate through their general action on body cells (adrenalin and thyroxine increase metabolic rate).

Hypothermia (page 60)

1. Exposure to low temperatures even for a short time without insulation will lead to hypothermia. Even temperatures of 15 to 20°C may cause hypothermia if a person is exposed long enough without protection. Exposure to water will cause hypothermia far more quickly than the same temperature in air as heat is more easily conducted away from the body.

2 (a) Short and stocky

(b) A short, stocky shape has a lower SA:V ratio and so loses heat more slowly.

3. Methods include passive rewarming (using a person's own body heat) for mild hypothermia, active external rewarming (using external heating) for moderate hypothermia and active internal rewarming (using devices to warm body fluids internally) for severe hypothermia. Using an incorrect method may cause premature dilation of blood vessels and so cause a reduction in blood pressure as well as a further drop in body temperature.

Control of Blood Glucose (page 61)

1. (a) Stimulus: Rise in the levels of glucose in the blood above a set level (about 5.5 mmol per L).
   (b) Stimulus: Fall in blood glucose levels below a set level (about 3.5 mmol per L).
   (c) Glucagon brings about the production (and subsequent release) of glucose from the liver by the breakdown of glycogen and the synthesis of glucose from amino acids.
   (d) Insulin increases glucose uptake by cells and brings about production of glycogen and fat from glucose in the liver.

2. Fluctuations in blood glucose (BG) and blood insulin levels are closely aligned. Following a meal, BG rises sharply and there is a corresponding increase in blood insulin, which promotes cellular glucose uptake and a subsequent fall in BG. This pattern is repeated after each meal, with the evening meal followed by a gradual decline in BG and insulin over the sleep (fasting) period. Negative feedback mechanisms prevent excessive fluctuations in blood glucose (BG) throughout the 24 hour period.

3. Negative feedback regulation.

4. With a lack of insulin (or lack of response to insulin), the body's cells are unable to take up glucose from the blood and, as a result, blood glucose remains high.

5. Type 1 diabetes arises because of a complete lack of insulin (destruction of beta cells) and is treated with the regular injection of insulin to enable the body to take up and utilize glucose after meals. Type 2 diabetes is the result of insulin resistance, i.e. the cells no longer respond to insulin or respond at too low a level. Treatment is centered around controlling the factors exacerbating the diabetes: controlling weight and diet, and increasing exercise, although anti-diabetic drugs and insulin therapy may be needed in severe cases,

6. The increase in type 2 diabetes has been associated with increasingly sedentary lifestyles, and the increasing proportion of overweight and obese people in the population. This proportion is now very high (more than 50% in some cases), so much so that young people are increasingly being diagnosed with type 2 diabetes (in previous decades, it was a disease of late middle age).

7. High blood glucose levels have several metabolic effects including ketoacidosis (low blood pH) as a result of metabolizing body fats (in place of glucose), risk of atherosclerosis associated with greater volumes of fat being transported, damage to blood vessels and nerves (resulting in loss of vision or gangrene).

Blood Clotting (page 63)

1. (a) Prevents bleeding and invasion of bacteria.
   (b) Aids in the maintenance of blood volume.

2. (a) Injury exposes collagen fibers to the blood.
   (b) Chemicals make the surrounding platelets sticky.
   (c) Clumping forms an immediate plug of platelets preventing blood loss.
   (d) Fibrin clot traps red blood cells and reinforces the seal against blood loss.

3. (a) Clotting factors catalyze the conversion of prothrombin to thrombin, the active enzyme that catalyzes the production of fibrin.
   (b) If clotting factors were always present, clotting could not be contained; blood would clot when it shouldn't.

4. (a) and (b) provided below. The first is the obvious answer, but there are disorders associated with the absence of each of the twelve clotting factors:
   (a) Classic hemophilia
   (b) Clotting factor VIII (anti-hemophilic factor)
   (a) Hemophilia B (Christmas disease)
   (b) Clotting factor IX (Christmas factor).

Temperature Regulation in Plants (page 64)

1. (a) Dormancy: growth stops to conserve energy during resource shortages or extremes of temperature.
   (b) Stratification: seeds do not germinate until they are exposed to a period of low temperatures.
   (c) Vernalization: budding and flowering does not occur until plants have been exposed to a period of low temperatures.

2. Stratification ensures the plant will germinate during warmer weather (after cold, wet period has passed) when the chances of survival are enhanced.

3. (a) Some plants use an alternative electron transport chain where the energy produced makes heat instead of ATP.
   (b) Any of: Provides warmth for pollinator, enables plant to melt snow or frost around it so it increases plant's survival chances, helps to disperse floral scent (so attracts pollinators).

KEY TERMS: Word Find (page 65)

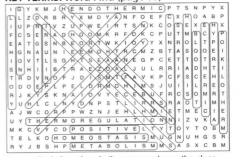

Answer list below given in the same order as the clues in the student workbook: blood clot, stratification, countercurrent, diabetes mellitus, dormancy, ectotherm(ic), endotherm(ic), fibrin, glucagon, hemostasis, homeostasis, homeotherm, hypothalamus, hypothermia, insulin, life history, metabolism, negative, poikilotherm, positive, thermoregulation, vernalization.

Plant Structure in Relation to Function
(page 68)

1. (a) **Stems**: Link the roots to the leaves. Provide support for the leaves, fruits, and flowers. Conduct water and dissolved minerals and foods around the plant. Produce new tissue at meristems.
   Leaves: Collect the sun's energy and convert it to usable energy (sugar). Control the entry and exit of gases and water vapor (therefore have a role in cooling the plant).
   Roots: Anchor the plant. Absorb water and dissolved minerals. Sometimes store food. Produce new tissue at meristems.

   (b) Materials transported: Water, minerals (e.g. N, P), sugar, essential ions (e.g. K^+, Na^+).

   (c) Functions of transport tissues: **Xylem**: Transports water and dissolved minerals, plant support.
   Phloem: Transports sugar (in solution), but also minerals, hormones, and amino acids, plant support.

2. Water

3. The amount of support tissue, the extent of the root system to supply water and minerals, the leaf density and spread (for light capture), and absence of disease will all determine ability to reach genetic potential.

Gas Exchange in Plants (page 69)

1. Carbon dioxide.

2. **Lenticels** allow gas exchange to occur through the otherwise impermeable woody tissue.

3. Thin, high surface area, loosely packed mesophyll.

4. (a) Terrestrial: Must limit water loss to the environment while still permitting the entry of carbon dioxide.
   (b) Aquatic: Maximizing uptake of gaseous CO_2 by reducing barriers to diffusion (most CO_2 in water is present as bicarbonate and is not freely dissolved).

5. (a) Thin, finely divided leaves increase surface area for gas exchange via diffusion across leaf surfaces. Lack cuticle on the leaves.
   (b) Breathing roots (pneumatophores) extending above the mud with lenticels in the woody tissue.

Gas Exchange and Stomata (page 70)

1. (a) Net gas exchange (no photosynthesis): Net use of oxygen and net production of carbon dioxide.
   (b) Net gas exchange (photosynthesis): Net use of carbon dioxide and net production of oxygen.

2. (a) Facilitate diffusion of gases into and out of the leaf.
   (b) Provide a large surface area for gas exchange.

3. Stomata regulate the entry and exit of gases into and out of the leaf and help in regulating water loss.

4. (a) **Stomatal opening**: Active transport of potassium ions into the guard cells (which lowers their solute (therefore water) potential) is followed by influx

of water. This causes the guard cells to swell and become turgid. The structure of the guard cell walls causes them to buckle out, opening the stoma.

   (b) **Stomatal closure**: Potassium ions leave the guard cell (making the solute (therefore water) potential of the guard cells less negative) and water follows by osmosis. The guard cells become flaccid and sag together closing the stoma.

Leaf and Stem Adaptations (page 72)

1. (a) Stomata
   (b) Stomata are the entry and exit point of gases into and out of the leaf. Without stomata, the plant could not carry out the gas exchanges (particularly obtaining CO_2) required for photosynthesis.

2. (a) Sun plant.
   (b) Compensates by having a much higher level of photosynthesis (sugar production).

3. Sun plants have adaptations for growth in full sunlight (photosynthesis with minimal sun damage to the leaves). The plants have thick leaves, with two layers of palisade mesophyll, and the chloroplasts are restricted mostly to the palisade mesophyll. The leaves absorb light and synthesise sugars rapidly, which compensates for the higher energy cost of producing thick leaves. Shade plants have adaptations for growth at low light intensities. The leaves thin and broad for maximum light capture. The palisade mesophyll layer is only one cell layer thick and chloroplasts occur throughout the palisade and spongy mesophyll. The rate of sugar production in these leaves is lower than in sun adapted leaves, but this is matched by the lower energy cost of maintaining the leaf.

4. (a) and (b) any two of the following:
   - Stomata occur in pits on the underside of the leaf.
   - The stomata are sunken into the surface of the leaf.
   - The stomata occur in grooves in the leaf.
   All these adaptations act to increase the humidity around the stomata more than they restrict the carbon dioxide uptake.

5. Photosynthetic stems have (any two):
   - Air spaces occur in the cortex (these are normally a feature of leaf tissue). Air spaces allow rapid diffusion of gases into and out of the leaf (necessary for continued photosynthesis).
   - Stomata in the leaf epidermis; again, these permit entry of carbon dioxide into the stem tissue.
   - Photosynthetic stem tissue is green (contains chloroplasts necessary for photosynthesis).

6. (a) Cacti
   (b) The leaves have become reduced to spines, which minimizes water loss, while the specialised stem takes over the role of photosynthesis.

7. Air spaces provide buoyancy to maintain the photosynthetic parts of the plant in the photic zone.

Excretion in Plants (page 74)

1. (a) Oxygen, CO_2, water.   (b) Diffusion

2. (a) They are used to create lignin, a component of wood (a strengthening tissue).
   (b) Storage of wastes make the leaves unpalatable and

tough, serving to deter grazers.

3. In the periderm (bark, wood), in the cell walls (especially of leaves), in the vacuoles of the cells.

Xylem and Phloem (page 75)
1. Xylem is strengthened by having hard fiber cells and spiral thickening of the vessel walls.

2. In gymnosperms, the only conducting cells in the xylem are tracheids, whereas the xylem of angiosperms contains both tracheids and vessel elements.

3. The perforations of the sieve plate enable the sugar solution to pass through and along the sieve tubes.

4. (a) The sieve tube.
   (b) The companion cell keeps the sieve tube cell alive and controls its activity.

5. Xylem is a dead tissue (the cells have lost the nucleus, organelles, and cytoplasm), while phloem is alive (some cells remain fully functional). Xylem transports water and dissolved minerals around the plant (from roots to leaves), whereas phloem conducts dissolved sugar around the plant from its place of production to where it is required.

Angiosperm Root Structure (page 76)
1. **Root hairs** increase the surface area for absorption.

2. Cap of cells protects the dividing cells behind the root cap, which are delicate and are easily damaged. The cap of cells also has a role in lubricating the root tip and facilitating root movement through the soil.

3. (a) and (b), any two of:
   - Dicot roots have primary xylem forming a star shape in the root center (with usually 3 or 4 points).
   - In dicot roots, the vascular tissue forms a central cylinder through the root (stele).
   - In dicots, the stele is surrounded by a pericycle.
   - In monocot roots, there are many xylem points.
   - In monocots, the stele forms a large ring of vascular tissue (stele), which surrounded by a very prominent and heavily thickened endodermis.
   - In monocots, there is no pericycle.
   - Monocots have a central pith inside the ring of vascular tissue.

4. A large cortex.

5. Parenchyma cells store starch and other substances.

Uptake in the Root (page 77)
1. (a) Passive absorption of minerals along with the water and active transport.
   (b) **Apoplastic** pathway (about 90%); water moves through the xylem and the spaces within cell walls. **Symplastic** pathway; water moves through the cell cytoplasm from cell to cell via plasmodesmata.

2. Large water uptake allows plants to take up sufficient quantities of minerals from the soil. These are often in very low concentration in the soil and low water uptakes would not provide adequate quantities.

3. (a) The **Casparian strip** represents a waterproof

barrier to water flow through the apoplastic pathway into the stele. It forces the water to move into the cells (i.e. move via the symplastic route).
   (b) This feature enables the plant to better regulate its uptake of ions, i.e. take up ions selectively. The movement of ions through the apoplast cannot be regulated because the flow does not occur across any partially permeable membranes.

Plant Mineral Requirements (page 78)
1. **Nitrogen**: Component of amino acids, proteins, nucleic acids, nucleotides, chlorophylls, and coenzymes.
   Potassium: Involved in osmosis and ion balance, and in opening and closing of stomata, activator of many enzymes.
   Magnesium: Part of the chlorophyll molecule, activator of many enzymes.
   Calcium: Component of cell walls, enzyme cofactor, involved in cellular membrane permeability, component of calmodulins (small proteins needed for the activities of cellular enzymes), regulator of membrane and enzyme activities.
   Sulfur: Component of some amino acids and proteins and of coenzyme A.
   Phosphorus: Component of energy carrying phosphate compounds (ATP/ADP), nucleic acids, several essential coenzymes, and phospholipids.

2. Mineral availability to plants include: Mutualistic associations with mycorrhizal fungi or bacteria (phosphorus and nitrogen respectively); the atmosphere (carbon and oxygen); artificially applied fertilizers; soils, rock weathering etc.

3. (a) Mycorrhizae extend the surface area available for mineral absorption by the plant.
   (b) Phosphorus may be limiting in those plants without a mutualistic mycorrhizal association.

Transpiration in Plants (page 79)
1. (a) They take up water by the roots.
   (b) Any one of:
   - Transpiration stream enables plants to absorb sufficient quantities of the minerals they need (the minerals are absorbed with the water and are often in low concentration in the soil).
   - Transpiration helps cool the plant.

2. Water moves by osmosis in all cases. In any order:
   (a) **Transpiration pull**: Photosynthesis and evaporative loss of water from leaf surfaces create a more negative water potential in the leaf cells than elsewhere in the plant, facilitating movement of water along a gradient in water potential towards the site of evaporation (stomata).
   (b) **Capillary effect/cohesion-adhesion**: Water molecules cling together and adhere to the xylem, creating an unbroken water column through the plant. The upward pull on the sap creates a tension that facilitates movement of water up the plant.
   (c) **Root pressure** provides a weak push effect for upward water movement.

3. High wind, high light, high temperature, and low humidity all increase evaporation rates.

4. The system excludes air. As the plant loses water through transpiration, it takes up water from the flask

via roots (or cut stem). The volume removed from the flask by the plant is withdrawn from the pipette. This can be measured on the pipette graduations.

5. (a) Measurements were taken at the start and at the end of the experiment in the same conditions (still air, light shade, 20°C). These rates should be the same (give or take experimental error). This indicates that the plant has not been damaged by the experiment and any results are therefore a real response to the experimental conditions.

(b) Moving air and bright sunlight increase transpiration rate, because they increase the rate of evaporation from the leaves. Bright sunlight also increases photosynthetic rate, which acts to increase solute concentration in the leaves.
Note: Lower humidity could also be said to increase transpiration rate (by increasing evaporative loss), but this would need to be tested further, i.e. the results here do not conclusively show this. Another test where the effects of darkness and humidity level were separated would be required. This is a good discussion point for students investigating experimental design and interpretation of results.

(c) Humid conditions reduce evaporative loss, dark conditions stop photosynthetic production of sugars (therefore solute concentration in the leaves decreases). Both these act to reduce transpiration rate by reducing the concentration gradient for water movement.

Investigating Plant Transpiration (page 81)

1. (a) Plot of data below.

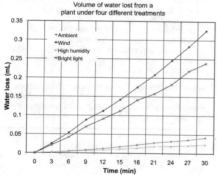

Volume of water lost from a plant under four different treatments

(b) Independent variable: Time. Explanatory note: Environmental conditions are manipulated in that there are different treatments, but each condition constitutes a controlled variable (or treatment).

2. (a) Transpiration rate in ambient conditions.
(b) An experimental control enables a measure of the biological response in the absence of any of the manipulated variables being tested (no treatment). This serves as a reference point.
(c) Wind and bright light increased water loss above the ambient (control) conditions.
(d) Wind and bright light increase transpiration rate by increasing evaporative loss from the leaves. High humidity reduces transpiration loss by reducing the gradient in water concentration from leaf to air (this

decreases evaporation).
(e) In humid conditions, there is a reduced gradient in water concentration between leaf and air, so the rate of diffusion of water vapor from the leaf to the environment will be slower (according to the laws governing diffusion rates).

Translocation (page 83

1. (a) Source to sink: This means the sugar flows from its site of production (in the leaves) to its site of unloading (at the roots).
(b) Usual source: Leaves and sometimes stems.
Usual sink: Roots.
(c) Other sources: Tubers or other storage organs from which sugar may be mobilized when photosynthetic tissues are absent.
(d) Other sinks: Fruits where sugar is required to form the succulent tissues of the fruit.

2. The energy is required to generate the gradient in H^+ that is used to drive the transport of sucrose into the transfer cell.

3. (a) **Translocation**: The transport (around the plant) of the organic products of photosynthesis.
(b) The bulk movement of phloem sap along a gradient in hydrostatic pressure (generated osmotically).
(c) The coupling of sucrose transport (into the transfer cell) to the diffusion of H^+ down a concentration gradient (generated by a proton pump).

4. The increase in dissolved sugar in the sieve tube cell increases its solute concentration (lowers water potential). Because of this, water moves into the sieve tube cells by osmosis (water moves to regions of higher solute concentration/more negative water potential).

5. The transfer cell uses active transport mechanisms (coupled transport of sucrose) to accumulate sucrose to levels 2-3 times those in the mesophyll. The sucrose then moves into the sieve tube cell.

6. Xylem sap is only water and dissolved minerals; phloem sap is a 30% sugar (mainly sucrose) solution.

7. Transport of sugars in the phloem is active and requires energy to be expended. For this, the tissue must be alive. Movement of water in xylem is a passive process.

8. If sap moved by pressure-flow, then there should be selective pressure for the sieve plate to be lost or become less of a barrier, yet this has not happened. (Of course, there are also selective pressures that operate against loss of the sieve plate, e.g. the need to have discrete yet freely communicating cells).

Investigating Plant Growth (page 85)

1. Concentration of fertilizer. Range: 0.0-0.30 g L^{-1} in steps of 0.06 g L^{-1}

2. 5

3. Outlying value: 23.6. This value should not be used in calculations as it is likely it is a chance event. Further replications of the experiment would identify if this value is a chance event or a true result.

4. Missing values below. For treatment 0.24 g L^{-1} values are with outlier included (without outlier):

Fertilizer concentration	Total mass	Mean mass
0.0	408.5	81.7
0.06	546.3	109.3
0.12	591.4	118.28
0.18	510.1	127.5
0.24	582.5 (558.9)	116.5 (139.7)
0.30	610.4	122.1

Fertilizer concn	Mean	Median	Mode
0.06	15.6	16	16
0.12	16.6	17	17
0.18	18.2	18	18
0.24	18.5	18.5	No mode
0.30	18.2	18	No mode

10. 0.24 g L-1 fertilizer (after removing the outlier).

11. Not all plants in sample may have received the same amount of fertilizer/water. Plants in centre of group may be more shaded/protected.

12. Nitrogen fertilizer increases the growth of radish plants, but only up to a limit, with peak performance reached at 0.24 g L-1 of fertilizer. The fertilizer also increases the number of leaves per plant (up to a limit) which is likely related to the overall increase in growth of the plant.

13. Replication decreases the likelihood of chance events affecting the results (or may identify true results that may have been attributed to chance). It helps to remove uncontrollable variables and adds weight to the findings.

5. Completed graph below. The first shows the outlier included and the second shows the outlier excluded. Answer depends on student choice in question 3.

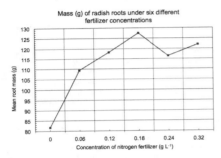

Mass (g) of radish roots under six different fertilizer concentrations

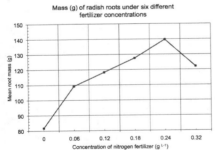

Mass (g) of radish roots under six different fertilizer concentrations

6. The students should have recorded the dry mass of the root, by first drying the root in an oven at low temperature to remove any water..

7. Measuring only the root mass fails to take into account the amount of growth/mass in the leaves.

8. Measuring the mass of the leaves, the number of leaves, the diameter on the root, the length of the root, the length of the leaves *etc*.

9.

Fertilizer concn	Mean	Median	Mode
0.0	8.6	9	9

Adaptations of Hydrophytes (page 88)
1. (a) Air spaces aid flotation and provide high surface area for diffusion of gases into (and out of) the photosynthetic tissues.
   (b) Thin (or absent) cuticle presents no barrier to the diffusion of gases into the leaves.
   (c) High stomatal densities on the upper leaf surface allow diffusion of carbon dioxide from the air into the inside of the leaf.

2. Water loss through transpiration is not an problem for hydrophytes because they are partially or fully submerged in water. Any water lost via transpiration can easily be replaced in their aquatic environment.

Adaptations of Xerophytes (page 89)
1. **Xeromorphic** adaptations allow xerophytes to survive and grow in areas with low or irregular water supplies.

2. (a)-(c) any of:
   - Modification of leaves to reduce transpirational loss (e.g. spines, curling, leaf hairs).
   - Shallow, but extensive fibrous root system to extend area from which water is taken and to take advantage of overnight condensation.
   - Water storage in stems or leaves.
   - Rounded, squat shape of plant body to reduce surface area for water loss.

3. The CAM metabolism (found in xerophytic plants, many of which are succulents) allows CO_2 to be fixed during the dark. This produces organic acids which accumulate in the leaves and later release CO_2 into the Calvin cycle during daylight (when light energy is available to provide H^+ and ATP for photosynthesis).

The stomata can then remain closed during the day when transpirational losses are highest.

Teacher's note: CAM and C4 metabolism are similar but CAM concentrates organic acids in time (at night so CO_2 is released in the day) whereas C4 plants concentrate CO_2 spatially, with a RuBisCO reaction center in the bundle sheath.

4. A moist microenvironment reduces the concentration gradient for evaporation from the leaf to the air, so there is less tendency for water to leave the plant.

5. In a high salt environment (often also exposed and windy), free (physiologically available) water is in short supply. Sea shoreline plants therefore have many xeromorphic adaptations.

KEY TERMS: Mix and Match (page 91)

active transport (AA), bulk flow (O), capillary action (L), Casparian strip (Y), companion cells (I), cortex (D), endodermis (P), flaccid (A), gas exchange (N), guard cells (J), hydrophyte (BB), mineral (T), osmosis (C), phloem (Q), pressure-flow hypothesis (E), root hair (X), root pressure (W), sieve tube cells (H), stomata (K), tracheid (S), translocation (R), transpiration pull (U), tension-cohesion hypothesis (M), turgid (V), vessel (B), xerophyte (F), xylem (G).

The Need for Gas Exchange (page 93)

1. **Cellular respiration** refers to the production of ATP through the oxidation of glucose. **Gas exchange** refers to the way in which respiratory gases (oxygen and carbon dioxide) are exchanged with the environment. Oxygen is required to drive the reactions of cellular respiration. Carbon dioxide is a waste product.

2. (a) Oxygen and carbon dioxide.   (b) Diffusion.

3. A gas exchange surface provides a surface across which gases can diffuse.

4. (a) Large surface area to provide for a large amount of gas exchange (to meet the organism's needs).
   (b) Thin membrane that does not present a large barrier to diffusion of gases.
   (c) Associated with mechanisms (e.g. blood flow) to maintain the concentration gradient.

Gas Exchange in Animals (page 94)

1. (a) Provides adequate supply and removal of respiratory gases necessary for an active lifestyle.
   (b) Enables animals to attain a larger size (as they are freed from a dependence on direct diffusion of gases across thin body surfaces).

2. (a) Air breathers produce mucus that keeps the gas exchange surface moist.
   (b) Some water vapor is present in lungs as a result of metabolism.

3. Gills are external structures and need support from a dense medium (water). In air, they would collapse.

4. Breathing in and out keeps air moving and maintains the concentration gradient for the diffusion of gases (carbon dioxide out and oxygen in).

Gas Exchange in Insects (page 95)

1. In insect tracheae, gases move by diffusion directly into the tissues. Gases diffuse into and out of the fluid at the end of the tracheole, and the fluid acts as the medium for gas exchange into the tissues.
   At rest, the fluid moves into the tracheoles, oxygen diffuses into the fluid and CO_2 diffuses out. When the muscles contract, the fluid is drawn into the tissues, and oxygen can diffuse into the tissues while CO_2 diffuses out into the fluid.

2. Valves present in the spiracles control the rate of entry and exit of air into and out of the tracheal system. This enables the rate of gas exchange to be regulated according to the changing activity levels (and therefore gas exchange requirements) of the insect.

3. Ventilation occurs when the insect makes rhythmic body movements. This helps to move the air in and out of the tracheae.

4. Tracheal systems provide direct delivery of oxygen to the tissues, without relying on a circulatory fluid combined with a respiratory pigment. This system is rapid and efficient for small organisms and has the advantage of reducing the reliance on water (water is a necessity for organisms relying on diffusion across a moist body surface). A reduced dependence on freely available water has allowed insects to colonize some of the driest, most inhospitable places on Earth.

5. (a)-(c) any of, in any order:
   - Tracheal gills increase surface area for gas exchange, e.g. aquatic insect larvae such as mayfly larvae. Note that the anal and caudal "gills" of some aquatic insects are involved in osmoregulation.
   - Trapped air beneath the wings provides an oxygen store above the spiracles, e.g. *Dytiscus*.
   - A plastron formed by a layer of air trapped against the spiracles by hydrofuge hairs. A plastron forms a non-compressible gill into which gases can diffuse, e.g. adult hydrophilid beetles.
   - Siphons to the water surface provide a link between the spiracles and the air above, e.g. mosquito larvae.

6. Physiological adaptation: Presence of a respiratory pigment (hemoglobin) either in the blood (*Chironomus*) or in the abdomen (*Anisops*).

Gas Exchange in Fish (page 97)

1. (a)-(c) any of, in any order:
   - Greatly folded surface of gills (high surface area).
   - Gills supported and kept apart from each other by the gas exchange medium (water).
   - Water flow across the gill surface is opposite to that of the blood flow in the gill capillaries (countercurrent), facilitating oxygen uptake.
   - Pumping mechanism of operculum aids movement of the water across the gas exchange surface.

2. (a) It maintains the diffusion gradient.
   As blood flows through the gill capillaries (gaining oxygen) it encounters blood of increasing oxygen content, so a diffusion gradient is maintained across the entire gill surface.
   (b) Diffusion into the blood would stop too soon. Parallel flow would result in rapid equilibration of oxygen saturation between the blood and the water and diffusion across the surface would stop.

3. (a) Moving water across the gill surface.
   (b) Ventilation prevents stagnation of the water at the gill surface and maintains the concentration gradient necessary for continued gas exchange.
   (c) **Pumping**: Operculum acts as a pump, drawing water past the gill filaments.
   Continuous swimming: Continuous (usually rapid) swimming with the mouth open produces a constant flow of water over the gill filaments.
   (d) These fish rely on being able to swim rapidly and continuously to provide the necessary ventilation of their gill surfaces. If they do not have the room to do this they will asphyxiate and die.

4. Oxygen availability in water is low anyway, so anything that lowers oxygen level further (high temperature or decomposition) increases the vulnerability of fish to oxygen deprivation. This is especially so for fish with high oxygen requirements such as trout and salmon.

Gas Exchange in Mammals (page 99)

1. The large surface area is provided by the numerous, thin-walled alveoli arising from terminal bronchioles. The lung's airways are increasingly divided and this enables a great many alveoli to encompassed.

2. (a) Trachea: Strengthened with cartilage bands and lined with ciliated epithelium. Cartilage provides rigidity and resistance against compression, while the ciliated epithelium helps to move unwanted dust and debris away from the gas exchange area.
   (b) Bronchioles: Provide the many subdivisions leading to the alveoli where gas exchange occurs. They do not require strengthening so largely lack cartilage but have a lot of smooth muscle which enables them to dilate and constrict.
   (c) Alveoli: Thin walled sac which provides a high surface area for the exchange of gases. Elastic connective tissue allows the alveoli to expand and recoil and a surfactant on the inner surface decreases surface tension so that the alveoli can inflate and deflate without collapsing/sticking.

3. (a) 3.56%. The CO_2 is the product of cellular respiration in the tissue.
   (b) 5% difference (exhaled air lower in oxygen).
   (c) The exhaled air mixes with the dead air volume of the previous inhalation (which is high in O_2 but low in CO_2). This raises the O_2 content of the exhaled air and drops its CO_2 level slightly.

4. Surfactant reduces surface tension of the lung tissue. This counteracts the tendency of the alveoli to recoil inward and stick together after each expiration.

Breathing in Humans (page 101)

1. Breathing ventilates the lungs, renewing the supply of fresh (high oxygen) air while expelling air high in CO_2 (gained as a result of gas exchanges in the tissues).

2. (a) Quiet breathing: External intercostal muscles and diaphragm contract. Lung space increases and air flows into the lungs (inspiration). Inflation is detected and breath in ends. Expiration occurs through elastic recoil of the ribcage and lung tissue (air flows passively out to equalize with outside air pressure).

   (b) During forced or active breathing, muscular contraction is involved in both the inspiration and the expiration (expiration is not passive).

3. Water vapor

4. The elasticity of the lung tissue enables natural recoil of the lungs during quiet breathing so that expiration is a passive process not requiring energy.

5. Blood pH is a good indicator of high carbon dioxide levels, since increased CO_2 levels cause blood pH to fall. This indicates a need to increase respiratory rate to remove the CO_2 (and obtain more oxygen).

Gas Transport in Mammals (page 102)

1. (a) Oxygen is high in the lung alveoli and in the capillaries leaving the lung.
   (b) Carbon dioxide is high in the capillaries leaving the tissues and in the cells of the body tissues.

2. Hemoglobin binds oxygen reversibly, taking up oxygen when oxygen tensions are high (lungs), carry oxygen to where it is required (the tissues) and release it.

3. (a) As oxygen level in the blood increases, more oxygen combines with hemoglobin. However, the relationship is not linear: Hb saturation remains high across a wide range of partial pressures of oxygen.
   (b) When oxygen level (partial pressure) in the blood or tissues is very low, hemoglobin saturation declines markedly and oxygen is released (to the tissues).

4. (a) Fetal Hb has a higher affinity for oxygen than adult Hb (it can carry 20-30% more oxygen).
   (b) This higher affinity is necessary because it enables oxygen to pass from the maternal Hb to the fetal Hb across the placenta.

5. (a) The Bohr effect.
   (b) Actively respiring tissue consumes a lot of oxygen and generates a lot of carbon dioxide. This lowers tissue pH causing more oxygen to be released from the hemoglobin to where it is required.

6. Myoglobin preferentially picks up oxygen from Hb and is able to act as an oxygen store in the muscle.

7. Any two of: **Hemoglobin**, which picks up H^+ generated by the dissociation of carbonic acid. **Bicarbonate** alone (from this dissociation), and combined with Na^+ (from the dissociation of NaCl). **Blood proteins**.

Adaptations of Diving Mammals (page 104)

1. (a) Breathing out before diving prevents nitrogen from the lungs entering the blood. This avoids the problems of the narcotic effects of nitrogen and formation of nitrogen bubbles in the blood on ascent from the dive. Breathing out before diving also helps to reduce buoyancy, assisting the descent.
   (b) A diving human fills the lungs with air before diving.
   (c) Reducing heart rate during a dive has the effect of slowing blood flow and metabolic rate which conserves oxygen during the dive.

2. See the table below. Only answers required in the table (oxygen in mL kg^{-1}) have been provided.

Location	Seal	Human
Air in lungs	1.83	10.3
Blood	37.5	14.3
Muscle	9.0	3.4
Tissue water	3.33	2.9
Total	51.67	30.86

3. (a) The seal has very little of its oxygen store in the lungs whereas humans keep a large proportion of their oxygen store in the lungs during a dive.
   (b) This is because the seal breathes out before diving and so empties its lungs of air. It also has very high muscle hemoglobin (myoglobin).

Obtaining Food (page 105)

1. Several examples provided for each. There are others.
   (a) Sharp teeth to remove skin from prey animal.
   (b) Modified gill rakers to strain plankton.
   (c) Sharp claws to grip prey. Specialised types of teeth for biting, holding and shearing flesh.
   (d) Generalized mouthparts (no loss or fusion) adapted for chewing plant material.
   (e) Mouthparts, often with whiskers, and head shape for sucking up mud from underneath.

2. (a) Filter feeding: Obtaining nutrients from particles suspended in the water. *Baleen whale.*
   (b) Deposit feeding: Obtaining nutrients by sifting and/or ingesting sediment or detritus. *Dung beetle.*
   (c) Suction feeding: Obtaining nutrients by ingesting prey and its surrounding fluid. *Zooplantivorous fish.*
   (d) Bulk feeding: Obtaining nutrients by eating whole organisms. *Stoat (ermine).*
   (e) Fluid feeding: Obtaining nutrients by ingesting only the fluids of another organism. *Mosquito.*

3. Carp are deposit feeders and loosen sediment and plant material from the beds of lakes and rivers. This damages fragile benthic communities and increases the amount of suspended material in the water (reduces water quality).

Adaptations of Predators (page 106)

1. (a) Camouflage enables the predator to remain undetected by the prey until it has the opportunity to strike successfully.
   (b) Other adaptations of ambush predators include structural modifications to allow long strike reach (long legs and tongues) and behaviour to allow precise, very slow movements to approach prey without being detected (e.g. chameleons, mantids).

2. Behavioral: the antlion larvae builds pits in the sand to trap insects, and it hides in the soil so its prey cannot detect it. Structural: large jaws allow it to quickly capture prey that fall into its trap.

3. Physiological: use of echolocation to explore the environment and find prey. Behavioral: individual dolphins work cooperatively to drive prey into a dense ball, this increases the chances of catching prey.

Food Vacuoles and Simple Guts (page 107)

1. (a) There is a single opening through which food enters and exits.
   (b) There is no regional specialization in the gut.

2. (a) **Intracellular** digestion occurs with food vacuoles (following endocytosis of the food particles). **Extracellular** digestion involves secreting digestive enzymes into a lumen (cavity) where breakdown of the food occurs.
   (b) Intracellular digestion is too slow and inefficient to cope with the large quantities of food and high metabolic rates typical of most animals.

3. Extracellular digestion begins in the gut cavity in sea anemones and outside the body in *Dugesia*.

Parasitism (page 108)

1. (a) Parasitoids spend only part of their life cycle as parasites and often consume the host. Parasites live their entire life in or on the host and do not usually kill it.
   (b) The parasitoid is dependent on a specific host for a crucial part of its life cycle (usually the larval phase). The emerald cockroach wasp relies on a cockroach to provide food for its larva. The cockroach dies as a result of the interaction. Without the cockroach, the parasitoid could not complete its life cycle.

2. Blood may carry pathogens between hosts.

3. Vampire bats act like parasites in that they feed off a host, harming but not killing it. However, unlike true parasites, they are free-living. They do not live on they host but return to a roost after feeding.

Diversity in Tube Guts (page 109)

1. (a) Gizzard grinds food into smaller particles for digestion.
   (b) Stomachs and crops store food allowing it to pass slowly into the next region of the gut (the glandular stomach of vertebrates is also important in digestion).
   (c) Intestine (midgut in insects) is the main site for digestion of food and absorption of nutrients.

2. (a) A. 1   Liver
        2   Ileum (small intestine is acceptable)
        3   Left kidney
        4   Colon (large intestine is acceptable)
        5   Stomach
      B. 1   Rectum
        2   Duodenum
        3   Colon (large intestine is acceptable)
        4   Ileum (small intestine is acceptable)
        5   Liver
        6   Stomach
   (b) The pig.
   (c) Prominent liver, small and large intestine. Rectum dorsal to the small intestine. Absence of gizzard or crop; stomach prominent as the food storage organ.
   (d) Rats and pigs are both mammals.

Insect Mouthparts (page 111)

1. Labrum (anterior lip), mandibles and maxillae (modified paired appendages), and labium (lower lip).

2. Chewing, sucking (with or without piercing), sponging

(with or without piercing), and lapping.

3. (a) Chewing: locust, beetle
   (b) Sponging: housefly
   (c) Chewing/lapping: bee
   (d) Seizing/chewing: dragonfly
   (e) Sucking: moth
   (f) Piercing/sponging: biting fly
   (g) Piercing/sucking: mosquito, aphid, flea, cicada
   (h) Sucking with mouth hooks: maggot

4. **Insect A**: Housefly type
   (a) Maxillary palp   (c) Labium
   (b) Rostrum
   Insect B: Butterfly (moth might be acceptable, although the antennae are butterfly-like)
   (d) Antenna   (f) Compound eye
   (e) Maxillary proboscis
   Insect C: Mosquito
   (g) Antennae   (i) Leg
   (h) Proboscis sheath
   Insect D: Bee (actually a honeybee)
   (j) Galea   (l) Labial palp
   (k) Glossa (tongue)
   Insect E: Cockroach (any "generalized orthopteran", including grasshopper, is acceptable)
   (m) Antenna   (p) Maxillary palp
   (n) Maxilla   (q) Labrum
   (o) Mandible

5. Color as indicated below:

Mosquito

Shield bug

Honeybee

Butterfly

Housefly

Mouthparts key

 Labrum   Labium   Maxilla   Mandible

6. (a) Caterpillar diet: Foliage, sometimes flowers.
   Mouthparts: Relatively generalized chewing type, with strong jaws (mandibles).
   (b) Butterfly diet: Nectar
   Mouthparts greatly rearranged to a specialized maxillary proboscis, with loss or fusion of the other mouthparts.

The Teeth of Fish (page 113)

1. Fish are homodonts, mammals are heterodonts. Homodonts have teeth with identical morphology, they all have one purpose. Most mammals are heterodonts, they have different types of teeth for various uses, e.g. biting incisors, shearing canines, chewing premolars, chewing/grinding molars.

2. (a) Butterfly fish
   (b) Manta ray and other filter feeders
   (c) Sharks and other predatory fish e.g. piranha
   (d) Parrotfish
   (e) Lampreys

3. Shark's teeth are not attached securely to the jaw. The teeth continually fall out or are pulled out when attacking prey. To compensate, teeth continually develop in the gum lining and move forward. (A shark may go through 20,000 teeth in its life time.)

Digestion in Fish (page 114)

1. Keeping the internal organs at a higher temperature than the environment speeds up digestion and increases metabolism allowing a more active lifestyle. In great white sharks this means faster swimming, allowing them to capture fast swimming fish and mammals such as seals.

2. Water is an extremely efficient heat sink. Any heat developed in smaller fish is quickly lost to the environment, making it difficult to maintain a high body temperature. The smaller surface to volume ratio of large sharks enables them to retain heat more easily.

3. The shark's stomach temperature rose after feeding, suggesting that it may be able to raise the temperature of its stomach when needed and maintain it at a slightly lower temperature when not feeding.

Dentition in Mammals (page 115)

1. **GIANT ANTEATER**: **Diet**: termites and ants. **Adaptations**: Lacks teeth completely and instead has sticky tongue to gather insects.

2. **DOLPHIN**: **Diet**: fish. **Adaptations**: No requirement for chewing. The teeth grab and hold prey which is tossed down the throat. Therefore the teeth are all similar.

3. **TREE SHREW**: **Diet**: insects and worms. **Adaptations**: Sharp, pointy cusps on teeth for a snappy chewing motion which crushes the tough insect exoskeleton and chops worms up for swallowing.

4. **PIG Diet**: omnivorous (mixed diet). **Adaptations**: Molars able to crush fibrous food. Incisors for ripping vegetation plus tusks for grubbing in the ground.

5. **GREY WHALE**: **Diet**: (microcrustaceans. **Adaptations**: Brush-like fringed plates on the upper jaw (baleen). When the mouth closes, water is forced out and the plankton are trapped on the inside of the sieve.

6. **MOUNTAIN SHEEP**: **Diet**: rough vegetation and grasses. **Adaptations**: Lower incisors bite against the dental plate (horny pad) of tough skin tissue (just visible in photograph). The back molars and premolars are large for crushing fibrous plant material.

7. **LION**: **Diet**: meat. **Adaptations**: Sharp canines for holding the prey. Small incisors (kept all of the way). Premolar is modified as a carnassial tooth for tearing and biting. The molars are sharp (non-crushing).

8. **RABBIT**: **Diet**: herbs and grasses. **Adaptations**: Sharp, nipping incisors. The canines have been lost, leaving a large diastema. Grinding and crushing molars and premolars. Unwanted food is pushed out the diastema.

9. **BLACK AND WHITE RUFFED LEMUR: Diet:** leaves, fruit, and flowers (some nectar and seeds). **Adaptations:** Teeth are all quite similar with pointed cusps for chopping and crushing fruit.

Mammalian Guts (page 117)

1. The answers to this question will vary somewhat depending on the particular herbivore chosen. Answers below compare a carnivore gut with that of a ruminant (foregut fermenter), a cow.
   (a) Size of stomach: Large in a carnivore relative to total gut length; also large in the ruminant but expanded with extra chambers for microbial fermentation of cellulose.
   (b) SI: Relatively short and wide in carnivores; very long (10-12X body length) in ruminants.
   (c) Hind gut: Poorly developed in carnivores with reduced (or absent) caecum and short, simple colon. Hind gut of medium length and degree of development in a ruminant; fermentation in the hindgut not important but water absorption from large volumes of material is important.

2. (a) The teeth (any of):
   – Carnivores molars/premolars modified into carnassials for shearing, herbivore teeth flatter with large grinding surfaces, specialised for grinding and chewing.
   – Diastema in herbivores provides space to manipulate bulky food within the oral cavity.
   – In herbivores, there may be a horny pad against which the incisors act to clip vegetation.
   – Canines in carnivores are very large and modified to hold prey and bite down.
   (b) – The temporalis muscle of ruminants is small (little biting force is required) whereas the masseter is large to assist in chewing action.
   – The temporalis muscle of carnivores is large and provides most of the biting force. The masseter is relatively small and its primary role is in stabilizing the jaw, not chewing.

3. (a) Transit time affected by: Diet type (high fiber passes through more quickly), storage capacity of the gut (smaller volumes may reduce transit time).
   (b) A smaller volume gut and rapid transit time reduces weight. For kangaroos, this is very important in the effectiveness of their locomotory mode (hopping).

Microbes and Digestion in Mammals (page 119)

1. • Large rumen for storage of plant matter (structural).
   • Specialization of the stomach into four regions, each with a particular role (structural).
   • Mutualistic relationship with rumen microbes (physiological).
   • Regurgitates, rechews, and reswallows fermented plant material (behavioural/physiological).
   • Food is eaten quickly but rechewed in a leisurely fashion later (behavioral).
   • Obtains most of energy requirements from the volatile fatty acids released by microbial fermentation (physiological).
   • Obtains most of nitrogen requirements from digestion of microorganisms (physiological).
   • Abomasum (gastric digestion) has lysozyme to break down microbial cell walls (physiological).
   • Produces vast quantities of alkaline saliva to maintain rumen pH (physiological).
   • Rumen contracts rhythmically to mix plant material with microbes (physiological).

2. Chewing the cud breaks down the plant matter and exposes it to the microbes. It also stimulates digestion.

3. Alkaline saliva maintains the pH of the rumen at ~7 to provide the appropriate environment for the microbes. Without the saliva, the constant production of VFAs would cause the rumen pH to fall.

4. The ruminant and its microbes depend on each other and both benefit. The ruminant receives a source of energy (volatile fatty acids) and nitrogen from microbes. The microbes receive a constant stable environment in which to grow and reproduce and a source of energy (from the cellulose in plant material).

5. A daily rhythm means that soft faeces can be produced and immediately eaten in the safety of the burrow. The hard faeces can be eliminated outside the burrow while browsing, keeping the burrow free of faecal material.

6. Both ruminants and rabbits rely on the fermentation of cellulose by mutualistic microbes for their nutrition. Both gain a large proportion of their energy requirement from VFAs and both obtain nitrogen from digestion of the microbes themselves. In both, the region of the gut that houses the microbes is greatly enlarged. In rabbits, fermentation occurs in the hindgut in a enlarged caecum. VFAs are absorbed across the caecum wall. The rabbit relies on producing and ingesting special cecotropes from the anus to obtain the full benefits of the microbial fermentation. In the ruminant, fermentation occurs in the rumen, which is the enlarged first chamber of the stomach. VFAs are absorbed across the rumen wall. Partly fermented plant material is rechewed slowly (rumination) which breaks it down further and allows the microbes to continue working on the cellulose.

Digestion in Insects (page 121)

1. Fluid feeders all have some mechanism for eliminating the large fluid volumes in the diet so that nutrients can be concentrated.

2. Both termites and ruminants rely on a mutualistic relationship with microbes to digest the cellulose in their diet. In ruminants, the products of microbial digestion are directly available to the ruminant from the bacteria. In termites, the symbiosis is more complex, because the termite receives sugars from gut protozoa, which themselves rely on bacteria to digest the cellulose. In both cases, the gut microbes receive a source of energy (as cellulose) and a place to live.

The Human Digestive Tract (page 122)

1. Structures as follows:

A	Mouth and teeth	G Gall bladder
B	Salivary glands	H Colon (or large intestine)
C	Esophagus	I Small intestine
D	Liver	J Rectum
E	Stomach	K Appendix
F	Pancreas	L Anus

Region responsible for each stated function as follows:
(a) I - small intestine   (e) F - pancreas (or B)
(b) J - rectum   (f) D - liver
(c) H - colon   (g) B - salivary gland
(d) E - stomach

2. Position of sphincters below.

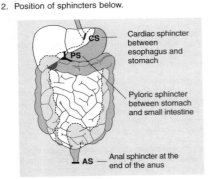

Cardiac sphincter between esophagus and stomach

Pyloric sphincter between stomach and small intestine

Anal sphincter at the end of the anus

3. (a) Lining (mucosa) of the stomach.
       Features: gastric gland.
   (b) Villi lining lumen of the small intestine (duodenum).
       Feature: Fingerlike villi project into the lumen. Layer of muscle visible below connective tissue of villi.
   (c) Liver. Feature: Bile ducts.

4. (a) Stomach: A three layered muscular wall to produce the movements to mix the food into chyme. Rugae allow expansion of volume. gastric glands specialized to produce acid, mucus, and pepsinogen (activated in acid to protein-digesting pepsin).
   (b) Small intestine: Fingerlike villi project into the lumen and provide large surface area for absorption of nutrients. Intestinal glands produce mucus to protect gut mucosa from damage and alkaline fluid to provide an appropriate pH for intestinal and pancreatic enzymes.
   (c) Large intestine: Simple columnar epithelium absorbs water from the slurry. Epithelium has many tubular glands which produce mucus to lubricate colon walls and aid feces formation. Strong muscular walls move material through the colon.

5. (a) and (b): any two of the following in any order:
   Site: Stomach   *Enzyme*: pepsin
   Purpose: Digestion of proteins to polypeptides.

   Site: Pancreas   *Enzyme*: pancreatic amylase
   Purpose: Digestion of starch to maltose.

   Site: Pancreas   *Enzymes*: trypsin/chymotrypsin
   Purpose: Digestion of proteins to polypeptides.

   Site: Pancreas   *Enzyme*: pancreatic lipase
   Purpose: Digestion of fats to fatty acids and glycerol.

   Site: Pancreas   *Enzymes*: peptidases
   Purpose: Digestion of polypeptides to amino acids.

   Site: Intestinal mucosa *Enzymes*: peptidases
   Purpose: Digestion of polypeptides to amino acids.

   Site: Intestinal mucosa *Enzymes*: maltase, lactase, sucrase
   Purpose: Digestion of carbohydrates (maltose, lactose,

sucrose respectively) into their constituent parts.

6. (a) The enzymes involved in digestion in different regions of the gut have specific **pH optima** (pH at which they operate most efficiently), so secretions are regionally pH appropriate. **Note**: For pepsin (stomach) this optimum is acid pH 1.5-2.0, for the enzymes in the small intestine, the optimum is alkaline pH 7.5-8.2.
   (b) The enzymes are secreted as inactive precursors in order to prevent their activity in the site of production and release (where they would damage the tissue). Once in the gut lumen, they can be activated to digest the food (the gut lining itself is protected by mucus).

7. (a) Food is moved through the gut by perstalsis (wave like contractions of smooth muscle).
   (b) Sphincters regulate the passage of food through the gut, allowing material to pass more quickly through the gut, or holding it back. Their activity depends on speed of digestion, food type, the influence of hormones, and the fullness of the gut.
   Note: Sphincter contraction partly or completely closes an orifice.

8. (a) Passage too rapid: Too little water is reabsorbed leading to diarrhea.
   (b) Passage too slow: Too much water is reabsorbed leading to compaction of the feces and constipation.

Control of Digestion (page 125)

1. (a) Food in the mouth causes a reflex stimulation of salivary glands and stomach (parasympathetic stimulation via the vagus). The effect is a marked increase in salivary and gastric secretion.
   (b) Presence of fat and acid in the small intestine stimulates release of cholecystokinin and secretin from the intestinal mucosa. These hormones inhibit gastric motility and stimulate the secretions of the pancreas, the production and release of bile, and the secretions of the intestinal glands.
   (c) Stretching of the stomach stimulates the reflex secretion of the hormone gastrin from the gastric mucosa. Gastrin acts back on the stomach to increase gastric secretion and motility.

2. The vagus nerve provides the parasympathetic innervation of the gut, stimulating salivary, gastric, and pancreatic secretion.

3. Nervous and hormonal mechanisms are both involved in coordinating and regulating digestion. The autonomic nervous system controls salivation, and stimulation of the stomach and pancreas via the vagus nerve increases secretions of these organs. Hormones are released in response to chemical or nervous stimuli and act on digestive organs to regulate the release of digestive secretions.

Adaptations for Absorption (page 126)

1. (a) Increasing the surface area of the gut increases the area available for nutrient absorption and therefore the rate at which food can be processed. Food cannot remain in the gut indefinitely, so efficient nutrient absorption enables the maximum gain from the food as it passes through.

(b) The type of food eaten, the metabolic requirements of the animal.

2. Some insects have gastric ceca, which are outpockets of the midgut, to increase the surface area for absorption. The number of ceca (2-200) is higher in more active insects. A semi-permeable membrane lines the midgut region (but not the fore- or hindgut), so nutrient absorption is restricted to this region. The ceca transfer nutrients to the hemolymph. Fish have two types of adaptations for increasing surface area of the intestine. Spiral valves (as in sharks) increase the surface area by turning the intestine into a series of coils instead of one straight tube. The number of turns in the valve corresponds to the fish's diet and activity level. Pyloric ceca increase the surface area with the walls of the pouches. Mammals have a long small intestine, which is coiled and looped to sit below the stomach. The intestinal wall is folded into microscopic finger-like structures called villi, which project into the lumen and greatly increase the surface area for absorption.

3. (a) Active transport
   (b) Facilitated diffusion
   (c) Active transport
   (d) Active transport
   (e) Active transport
   (f) Diffusion
   (g) Diffusion
   (h) Diffusion

Birds With Runny Noses (page 128)

1. Human kidneys are not efficient enough at concentrating salt in the urine. In order to remove the amount of salt in 1 L of seawater it would take 1.5 L of water from the body. The effect is dehydration.

2. Salt glands are found in the heads of reptiles and birds and remove excess salt from the blood. Salt is removed using active transport via a Na-K pump, which pumps salt form the blood into the duct of the gland. The salt is excreted from the nares in seabirds and from near the eyes in reptiles.

3. Salt glands in birds and reptiles are highly efficient at removing salt from the blood. They use a Na-K pump to concentrate the salt excretions to almost twice that of seawater. If a petrel was to drink 1 L of seawater it would gain about 0.5 L of fresh water. The kidneys of marine mammals are not as efficient as the salt glands of birds or reptiles but still produce a urine with a salt concentration higher than sea water's. A whale drinking 1 L of sea water gains about 0.3 L of fresh water.

Osmoregulation in Water (page 129)

1. Active transport of ions across gill surfaces. Ingestion of salt with food.

2. Osmoregulators regulate fluid balance by regulating or compensating for water fluxes (in and out). Example: Fish (bony and cartilaginous). Osmoconformers do not regulate body fluid composition and allow ion concentrations in their bodies to fluctuate with those of the environment. Example: Marine invertebrates although intertidal organisms may have some limited abilities to osmoregulate and/or tolerate wide salinities.

3. (a) Crabs placed in diluted seawater gained water osmotically because their body fluids are more concentrated than the seawater dilution. The rate of gain was greater in the 50% seawater solution. This is because the osmotic differential is greater than for the 75% dilution.
   (b) This crab species has limited capacity for osmoregulation, i.e. a limited ability to rapidly adjust the composition of its body fluids in a dilute environment.

Managing Fluid Balance on Land (page 129)

1. Water is gained by: Drinking, eating, production of water through metabolism (metabolic water), and withdrawal of water from the urine.

2. (a) Kidneys produce hypertonic urine. Sweat glands may be reduced to conserve water. Metabolism of fat stores provides water.
   (b) Skin is water impermeable. Excrete uric acid to conserve water. Nocturnal and /or seek shade to reduce evaporative water loss.
   (c) Waxy cuticle reduces water loss. Excrete uric acid to conserve water. Seek shade/underground/ nocturnal to reduce evaporative water loss.
   (d) Live in or near water or in moist conditions. May secrete wax and spread over body to reduce water loss. May aestivate below ground in dry weather.
   (e) Live underground to reduce exposure to heat. Live in moist soil. Form dense aggregations.

3. Structural adaptations are morphological features that reduce water loss. Behavioral adaptations are actions by the animal that help to conserve water. Physiological adaptations are metabolic processes that conserve water. These include:
   Structural: Waxy cuticle as a barrier to evaporative loss (arthropods). Thick fur/hair and oily skin secretions act as insulation to evaporative loss (mammals).
   Behavioral: Humidity/shade seeking behavior (arthropods, mammals). Hibernation/torpor (mammals). Nocturnal behavior (arthropods, mammals).
   Physiological: Long loop of Henle. Efficient water gain from metabolism. Tolerance to water loss.

4. Water can be lost via urine or feces, through airways, evaporation from sweat glands.

5. (a) Birds and mammals concentrate urine in the kidneys by creating salt gradient through the kidney tissue that enables water to be withdrawn from the urine. It is only in birds and mammals that the loop of Henle is long enough to produce a sufficient salt gradient for the osmotic withdrawal of enough water to concentrate the urine.
   (b) Kangaroo rats have an very long loop of Henle. This increases the extent of the salt gradient in the kidney so that a large volume of water can be reabsorbed from the urine.

Water Balances in Desert Animals (page 132)

1. Mammals need to drink regularly to replace losses through urination, defecation, and sweating.

2. Water requirement per day = 60 ml.

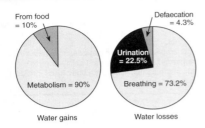

From food = 10%

Metabolism = 90%

Water gains

Defaecation = 4.3%

Urination = 22.5%

Breathing = 73.2%

Water losses

3. (a)-(c) any three of the following:
   - Able to meet most of their water requirements from oxidation of dry foods (metabolism).
   - Kidneys are able to produce very concentrated urine (long loop of Henle in the nephrons).
   - Reduce losses from breathing by reabsorbing moisture in the nasal passages.
   - Feces egested as very dry pellets.
   - Do not need to sweat or pant to keep cool.

4. Behavior, e.g. inactivity underground during the day.

Water Budget in Humans (page 133)

1. Metabolism involves the oxidation of glucose to produce ATP. A by-product of this process is water ($6O_2 + C_6H_{12}O_6 \rightarrow 6CO_2 + 6H_2O$)

2. (a) Intestinal infection resulting in diarrhea.
   (b) Inadequate access to fluids.
   (c) Excessive vomiting.
   (d) Excessive sweating.

3. Excessive water intake, without associated intake of electrolytes, has a diluting effect where there is an increase in total body water relative to the total amount of exchangeable sodium. This causes an osmotic shift of water from the plasma into the cells, particularly the brain cells. Typical symptoms include nausea, vomiting, headache and malaise. **Teacher's note**: As the hyponatremia worsens, confusion, diminished reflexes, convulsions, stupor or coma may occur. Nausea is, itself, a stimulus for the release of ADH, which promotes the retention of water, leading to a positive feedback loop and the potential for a vicious cycle of hyponatremia and its symptoms.

Nitrogenous Wastes in Animals (page 134)

1. Main source of nitrogen-containing wastes is the breakdown of nitrogen containing compounds (amino acids and nucleic acids).

2. (a) Uric acid has very low toxicity (it is almost completely non-toxic) and (unlike urea and ammonia) can be excreted with very little water loss. Because very little water is lost in its excretion, uric acid is ideal for terrestrial animals (it reduces their reliance on water availability).
   (b) Ammonia is highly toxic and cannot be held in the body's tissues.

3. The type of excretory product an animal produces is closely correlated with environment. **Ammonia** is a small, highly soluble molecule. It can be lost rapidly (by diffusion), at low energy cost, through surface contact

with the water, where its toxic effects are diluted. It is a common excretory product in aquatic invertebrates (which lose ammonia through the body surface) and the main excretory product in bony fish (which lose it through the gills). **Urea** is easily soluble and has a moderately low toxicity, so it can be held for some time in solution in the body fluids before excretion. This is a good strategy for terrestrial and semi-aquatic organisms (such as mammals and amphibians) that have (generally) retained a relatively high dependence on fresh water, and have the capacity to carry small volumes of urine along with them. **Uric acid** prevails in insects, land snails, most reptiles, and birds. All of these are typically terrestrial animals, and the formation of uric acid (which is of very low toxicity and solubility) can be seen as an adaptation to water conservation in a terrestrial habitat.

Invertebrate Excretory Systems (page 135)

1. (a) Flatworm: Protonephridia. Waste: Ammonia.
   (b) Insect: Malpighian tubules. Waste: Uric acid.
   (c) Earthworm: Nephridia. Waste: Ammonia and urea.

2. Uric acid follows active secretion of salts into the malpighian tubules. Water is absorbed from the waste fluid as it passes through the hindgut. When sufficient water has been withdrawn, the uric acid precipitates out as a paste.

3. Answer required for only one of the following:
   Flatworms live in wet environments so the ammonia produced is quickly diluted after it diffuses out.
   Annelids live in damp environments but have more tolerance to desiccation (than flatworms), hence the mix of urea and ammonia (urea lowers the toxicity of the excretory product).
   Insects are terrestrial and have a relatively high tolerance to dry environments. Wastes cannot diffuse away, so a waste product of low toxicity that can be excreted with minimal water loss is required.

Vertebrate Excretory Systems (page 135)

1. The gills.

2. (a) In a **marine** environment, **bony fish** tend to **lose** water by osmosis (body fluids are less concentrated than the environment). They must drink (salt) water to replace losses and therefore tend to gain excess salt. In fresh water, bony fish tend to gain water (body fluids more concentrated than the environment). They must void this water and they lose valuable ions in doing so.
   (b) Marine bony fish drink a lot of salt water to replace the water they lose by osmosis. The excess salts they gain in doing this are actively excreted across the gills. Freshwater bony fish do not drink at all and take up ions actively across the gills.

3. (a) Nephron
   (b) The large number of nephrons and their particular orientation in the mammalian kidney permits a large amount of water to be reabsorbed from the urine back into the blood. Mammals therefore can void a concentrated urine.

4. (a) The number of nephrons present.
   (b) The length of the loop of Henle.

5. In contrast to the kidneys of mammals, the kidneys of fish have very few nephrons, and these may often lack glomeruli. Functionally, fish kidneys can only produce a urine that is isotonic with the blood (the urine in fish cannot be concentrated, unlike the urine of mammals). The kidneys of mammals have many nephrons with loops of Henle of varying lengths, and the urine can be hypertonic to the blood.

6. (a) 25 minutes after drinking the water, urine volume had nearly doubled. After 50 minutes urine volume had increased more than threefold from the starting (reference) volume of 100 ml. After this time, urine volume declined steadily, returning to the reference volume after 150 minutes.

   (b) There is a time lag between drinking the water and clearing the majority of the excess fluid from the body. This represents the time taken for filtration of the blood and urine formation

The Urinary System (page 138)

1. The urinary system comprises the **kidneys**, which produce urine containing the products of excretion, the **renal blood vessels**, which transfer blood to and from the kidneys, the **ureters**, which carry urine to the bladder from the kidney, the **bladder**, which stores urine before it is passed out of the body, and the **urethra**, which conducts urine from the bladder to the outside of the body.

2. 99.4%

3. In maintaining its filtration rates, the kidney requires blood at a higher pressure than other organs because large quantities of fluid must be forced through the capillaries of the glomerulus.

4. Fatty connective tissue insulates and protects the kidneys from external damage, and anchors them firmly in place.

The Physiology of the Kidney (page 139)

1. (a) A nephron is a selective filtering element in the kidney.
   (b) Each nephron is divided into regions where the blood is filtered, and where the filtrate is modified by secretion and reabsorption. By these processes, the nephrons produce the excretory fluid, urine.

2. (a) **Glomerular filtration**: Produces an initial filtrate of the blood that is similar in composition to blood and can be modified to produce the urine.
   (b) **Active secretion**: **Required answer**: Secretion allows to get rid of unwanted substances into the urine. **Extra detail**: Active secretion of chloride in the ascending limb (with sodium following passively) contributes to the maintenance of the salt gradient in the extracellular fluid (this gradient allows water to be reabsorbed in the collecting duct). Secretion of toxins and unwanted ions into the filtrate in the distal tubules allows the blood composition to be adjusted and poisons to be excreted. Energy is used to secrete these substances against their concentration gradients.
   (c) **Reabsorption**: Essential process that allows the useful substances (required by the body) to be retained from the filtrate (particularly the initial

filtrate, where 90% is reabsorbed). The body would waste energy if these substances were not retained.
   (d) **Osmosis**: **Required answer**: Osmotic loss of water allows the urine to be concentrated (via loss of water). **Extra detail**: Osmosis is important in two regions of the nephron: In the descending limb of the loop of Henle, osmotic loss of water concentrates the filtrate so that salt can be withdrawn from the ascending limb to contribute to the salt gradient in the extracellular fluid. In the collecting duct, loss of water by osmosis provides the final concentration of the urine.

3. (a) The salt gradient allows water to be withdrawn from the urine (allows the urine to be concentrated). **Note**: Because the salt gradient increases through the medullary region, the osmotic gradient is maintained and water can be continually withdrawn from the urine.
   (b) Salt gradient is produced by the active and passive movement of salt from the filtrate into the extracellular fluid in the medulla.

Control of Urine Output (page 141)

1. (a) Diabetes insipidus is characterized by excretion of large amounts of very dilute urine (accompanied by a great thirst). The lack of ADH causes excessive urine production (ADH reduces urine output).
   (b) Diabetes insipidus is treated by administering ADH.

2. Alcohol inhibits ADH release causing greater urine output, resulting in dehydration and thirst.

3. The stimulation or inhibition of ADH release results in an adjustment of urine output until homeostasis is restored. The homeostatic adjustment made in response to the ADH release acts back on the hypothalamus to counteract any further change.

4. If the active transport of sodium and chloride ions is inhibited in the nephron, so too is the ability to establish the salt gradient required to withdraw water from the filtrate. As a result, the urine passes out without being concentrated.

KEY TERMS: Mix and Match (page 142)

alveoli (O), antidiuretic hormone (D), dentition (Y), digestive enzymes (F), excretion (M), extracellular digestion (G), gastric ceca (H), gastrovascular cavity (K), gills (J), gut (A), intestinal villi (T), intracellular digestion (Q), kidney (R), loop of Henle (N), lungs (Z), malpighian tubules (P), nephridia (L), nitrogenous waste (I), osmoregulation (E), parasite (S), predator (V), protonephridia (W), respiratory gas (X), respiratory membrane (B), spiral valve (U), tracheae (C).

Transport and Exchange Systems (page 144)

1. As body mass increases the surface area to volume ratio decreases. As this occurs diffusion becomes too inefficient and slow to provide raw materials quickly enough to all the cells of larger animals. Mass transport systems are required to transport materials to and from where they are needed.

2. (a) In vertebrates mass transport is used to transport materials around the body.
   (b) Mass transport systems allow materials to be

moved over a long distance in complex multicellular organisms. In contrast, small organisms such as the flatworm or single celled eukaryotes have a surface area to volume ratio large enough to allow for materials to be efficiently transported by diffusion.

(c) The **tissues** and either the **gills** or **lungs** (depending upon the animal).

Circulatory Fluids in Invertebrates (page 145)

1. (a) and (b), any two in any order: Clotting wounds, internal defense, transport of nutrients.

2. Vertebrate blood carries oxygen to the body tissues. Insect hemolymph generally does not.

3. Either of: Maintain body pressure to assist with molting and antifreeze for overwintering.

4. 10% of the hemolymph is cells whereas 40-50% of blood is cells.

Vertebrate Blood (page 146)

1. *Answers given may provide more detail than required.*
   (b) Protection against disease:
      Blood component: White blood cells
      Mode of action: Engulf bacteria, mediate immune reactions, and allergic and inflammatory responses.
   (c) Communication between cells, tissues and organs:
      Blood component: Hormones
      Mode of action: Specific chemicals which are carried in the blood to target tissues, where they interact with specific receptors and bring about an appropriate response.
   (d) Oxygen transport:
      Blood component: Hemoglobin molecule of erythrocytes.
      Mode of action: Binds oxygen at the lungs and releases it at the tissues.
   (e) Carbon dioxide transport:
      Blood components: Mainly plasma (most carbon dioxide is carried as bicarbonate in the plasma, a small amount is dissolved in the plasma). Red blood cells (a small amount (10-20%) of carbon dioxide is carried bound to hemoglobin).
      Mode of action: Diffuses between tissues, plasma, and lungs according to concentration gradient.
   (f) Buffer against pH changes:
      Blood components: Hemoglobin molecule of erythrocytes. Plasma bicarbonate and proteins.
      Mode of action: Free hydrogen ions are picked up and carried by the hemoglobin molecule (removed from solution). Plasma bicarbonate can form either carbonic acid by picking up a hydrogen ion (H^+), or sodium bicarbonate by combining with sodium ions. Negatively charged proteins also associate with H^+.
   (g) Nutrient supply:
      Blood component: Plasma
      Mode of action: Glucose is carried in the plasma and is taken up by cells (made available throughout the body to all tissues).
   (h) Tissue repair:
      Blood components: Platelets and leukocytes
      Mode of action: Platelets initiate the cascade of reactions involved in clotting and wound repair. Leukocytes (some types) engulf bacteria and foreign material, preventing or halting infection.
   (i) Hormone, lipid, and fat soluble vitamin transport:

Blood component: α-globulins
Mode of action: α-globulins bind these substances and carry them in the plasma. This prevents them being filtered in the kidneys and lost in the urine.

2. Any of: Presence (WBC) or absence (RBC) of **nucleus**. Color, reflecting presence (RBC) or absence (WBC) of respiratory pigment, **hemoglobin**. **Shape and size** (smaller, dish shaped RBCs vs larger, rounded WBCs. **Mitochondria** present in WBCs, absent in RBCs.

3. (a) Lack of a nucleus allows more space inside the cell to carry Hb (hence greater O_2 carrying capacity).
   (b) Lack of mitochondria forces the red blood cells to metabolize anaerobically so that they do not consume the oxygen they are carrying.

4. (a) Elevated eosinophil count: Allergic response such as hay fever or asthma.
   (b) Elevated neutrophil count: Microbial infection
   (c) Elevated basophil count: Inflammatory response e.g. as a result of an allergy or a parasitic (as opposed to bacterial) infection.
   (d) Elevated lymphocyte count: Infection or response to vaccination.

Adaptations of Vertebrate Blood (page 148)

1. 8% of body weight = .08 x 70 = 5.6 kg = 5.6 L.

2. Blood contains antifreeze glycoproteins. Blood contains no hemoglobin (but sufficient oxygen diffuses across scaleless skin).

3. Underground CO_2 can build up and O_2 become difficult to obtain. More efficient transport of CO_2 out of the body and O_2 into the blood allows moles to remain underground without the need to continually come to the surface.

4. Fish (especially migratory species) may encounter very variable environments (with respect to temperature, salinity, and oxygen level). Having several hemoglobin structures, each with a different capacity to bind oxygen, means they can quickly accommodate changes in environment, and continue to supply their tissues with oxygen efficiently.

5. Oxygen partial pressure must be higher.

Acid-Base Balance (page 149)

1. Blood is continuously circulating and carrying with it the products of metabolic activity (which are generally acidic and could potentially alter pH considerably if the blood were not buffered). The efficiency (and continuation) of metabolic processes depends on blood pH staying within the narrow range required by the enzymes catalyzing metabolic processes.

2. Metabolic acidosis is caused by increased production of H^+ by the body or the inability of the body to form bicarbonate (HCO_3^-) in the kidney. Causes can be varied by include diarrhea (loss of HCO_3^-), renal failure, starvation, and poisoning.

3. (a) Chemical buffers in the blood tie up excess H^+ or bases temporarily. The bicarbonate ion and its acid (carbonic acid) are in a dynamic equilibrium to mop up excess H^+ and OH^-. The system is supported by the charged groups on blood proteins, which act as

H⁺ acceptors or donors.

(b) If a base is added to the system, the OH⁻ is neutralized to a weak base (HCO_3^-)

4. (a) The respiratory response to excess H⁺ is an increase in the rate and depth of breathing.

(b) The excess H⁺ comes from the dissociation of carbonic acid (H_2CO_3), which arises as a result of carbon dioxide combining with water.

(c) Respiratory acidosis is the result of decreased ventilation of the pulmonary alveoli. This can arise as a result of airway obstruction (e.g. asthma), depression of the respiratory center (e.g. as a result of trauma), certain diseases (e.g. muscular dystrophy), and obesity.

5. It is only through the renal system that excess acids and bases can be permanently eliminated from the body; this is achieved mainly through excretion of hydrogen ions and reabsorption of hydroxide ions (since most metabolic wastes are acidic).

Blood Vessels (page 150)

1. (a) Veins have less elastic and muscle tissue than arteries.

(b) Veins have a larger lumen than arteries.

2. Most of the structural differences between arteries and veins are related to the different blood pressures inside the vessels. Blood in veins travels at low pressure and veins do not need to be as strong, hence the thinner layers of muscle and elastic tissue and the relatively larger lumen. **Teacher's note**: There is still enough elastic and muscle tissue to enable the veins to adjust to changes in blood volume and pressure.

3. (a) Capillaries are very small blood vessels forming networks or beds that penetrate all parts of the body. The only tissue present is an endothelium of squamous epithelial cells. In contrast, arteries have a thin endothelium, a central layer of elastic tissue and smooth muscle and a thick outer layer of elastic and connective tissue. Veins have a thin endothelium, a central layer of elastic and muscle tissue and a thin outer layer of elastic connective tissue. In addition, veins also have valves.

(b) Capillaries are not under any pressure from blood flow, but must be thin to allow efficient exchange of nutrients and wastes between the blood and tissue. **Note**: Arteries must be strong enough to withstand the high flow and pressure of blood pumped from the heart. Blood returning to the heart through veins is at a lower pressure, so less elastic and muscle tissue is required, but they contain valves to prevent blood backflow.

4. Blood flows in the same direction as the decreasing pressure gradient: arteries to capillaries to veins. Blood flow is thus slowest in the capillaries, which allows time for exchange of gases and nutrients. The rate, or velocity, of blood flow varies inversely with the total cross-sectional area of the blood vessels. As the total cross-sectional area of the vessels increases, the velocity of flow decreases. In blood vessels, most of the resistance opposing blood flow is due to vessel diameter. As vessel diameter decreases, the resistance increases and blood flow decreases. Very little pressure remains by the time blood leaves the capillaries and

enters the venules. Venous return therefore depends on skeletal muscle action, respiratory movements, and constriction of smooth muscle in venous walls.

5. Veins are "massaged" by the skeletal muscles. Valves (together with these muscular movements) help to return venous blood to the heart by preventing backflow away from the heart. Teacher's note: When muscles contract and tighten around a vein, the valves open and blood is driven towards the heart. When the muscles relax, the valves close, preventing backflow.

6. Venous blood oozes out in an even flow from a wound because it has lost a lot of pressure after passing through the narrow capillary vessels (with their high resistance to flow). Arterial blood spurts out rapidly because it is being pumped directly from the heart and has not yet entered the capillary networks.

7. Capillaries form dense networks in tissues with high metabolic rates to ensure sufficient exchange of gases and quick removal of wastes. This enables high metabolic rate to be maintained without the build up of toxic wastes or reduced supply of oxygen and nutrients.

Capillary Networks (page 152)

1. Capillaries are branching networks of fine blood vessels where exchanges between blood and tissue take place. Blood enters the network at the arteriolar end and is collected by venues at the venous end. The true capillaries form a network outside of the vascular shunt.

2. The smooth muscle sphincters regulate the blood flow to the capillary network by contracting to restrict blood flow to the network and relaxing to allow blood to flow in. The vascular shunt connects the arteriole and venule and allows blood to bypass the capillaries when the smooth muscle sphincters are contracted.

3. (a) Situation A would occur when the body is restricting blood flow to the capillaries, for example when trying to conserve heat by diverting blood away from the extremities.

(b) Situation B would occur when the body is trying to remove excess heat by diverting blood to the skin and extremities or when the body is trying to provide extra blood to areas of high metabolism, e.g. when exercising or digesting food.

4. A portal venous system drains blood from one capillary network into another. An example is the hepatic portal system which drains blood from the capillary network in the gut lumen to the capillary network in the liver. Normally capillary networks drain into veins that return directly to the heart.

The Formation of Tissue Fluid (page 153)

1. The tissue fluid bathes the tissues, providing oxygen and nutrients as well as a medium for the transport (away) of metabolic wastes, e.g. CO_2.

2. Capillaries are very small blood vessels forming networks or beds that penetrate all parts of the body. Capillary walls are thin enough to allow gas exchange between the capillaries and surrounding tissue.

3. (a) Arteriolar end: Hydrostatic pressure predominates in causing fluid to move out of the capillaries.

(b) Venous end: Increased concentration of solutes

and reduction in hydrostatic pressure at the venous end of a capillary bed **lowers the solute potential** within the capillary and there is a tendency for water and solutes to re-enter the capillary.

4. (a) Most tissue fluid finds it way directly back into the capillaries as a result of net inward pressure at the venule end of the capillary bed.
   (b) The lymph vessels (which parallel the blood system) drain tissue fluid (as lymph) back into the heart, thereby returning it into the main circulation.

Open Circulatory Systems (page 154)

1. Fluids are cycled through a heart into the body cavity where they bathe the tissues before moving back to the heart. Hemolymph moves along a dorsal blood vessel to a tubular heart where it is pumped through short vessels to the rest of the body. Hemolymph is assisted to move through the body by muscle movements and re-enters the vessel system through ostia.

2. Because the hemolymph is not contained in vessels it is not under pressure like in a closed circulatory system. As a result hemolymph only oozes slowly through splits in the cuticle.

3. Crustaceans have an advanced vessel system to the point where it is better described as incompletely closed. Insects have a relatively rudimentary vessel system and is much more open than crustaceans.

4. (a) The vessels open into the body cavity and mix with the tissue fluids.
   (b) There are many branched vessels in crustaceans that take hemolymph through the body. It mixes with tissue fluid for only a short time before draining into sinuses and reentering the vessel system.

Closed Circulatory Systems (page 155)

1. Unlike closed systems, open circulatory systems do not have a complete circuit of vessels for blood to pass through from the heart to the body and back again.

2. Blood passes from the gills to the body.

3. Blood returns to the heart after the lungs.

4. By passing blood back to the heart from the lungs, the double circuit system is able to maintain high blood pressure throughout the body. Higher systemic pressures are important for efficient oxygen delivery and processes like renal filtration.

5. (a) The fish heart is a single pump. Blood flows from the atrium to the ventricle.
   (b) The mammalian heart is a double pump with two atria and two ventricles separated by a muscular septum. One pump sends blood to the lungs, the other sends blood to the body.

6. Blood flow within vessels can be regulated by the contraction or relaxing of blood vessel walls. This enables animals to restrict blood flow in some areas and increase it in others in response to need.

7. Compare:
   Both annelids and vertebrates use closed circulatory systems and circulate blood through a series of vessels. Both systems contain contractile elements that move the blood through the vessels.
   Contrast:
   Vertebrates pump blood through vessels using the heart as the main pumping organ whereas annelids use the dorsal blood vessel as the main contractile element with assistance from the aortic arches.

8. Both insects and crustaceans have open circulatory systems. Insects have limited blood vessel development, while crustaceans have a well developed series of vessels, and the circulatory fluids spend only a short time outside of the vessel system. Annelids and cephalopods have closed circulatory systems. The annelid system is relatively rudimentary with no clearly defined heart, while cephalopods use a well developed heart and accessory hearts to pump blood between the gills and the body. From these comparisons it is possible to say that there is evidence of a gradient between fully open and fully closed systems.

The Human Circulatory System (page 157)

1. (a) Head   (d) Gut (intestines)
   (b) Lungs   (e) Kidneys
   (c) Liver   (f) Genitals/lower body

The Liver's Homeostatic Role (page 158)

1. (a)- (c) any of:
   For protein metabolism
   – Transamination of amino acids to create new, non-essential amino acids.
   – Deamination of excess amino acids and production of urea in the urea cycle.
   – Synthesis of plasma proteins.
   For carbohydrate metabolism:
   – Glycogenesis (formation of glycogen from glucose).
   – Glycogenolysis (breakdown of glycogen to form glucose (in the presence of glucagon)).
   – Conversion of glycogen to fats for storage.
   – Conversion of fats back to glycogen to enable mobilization of glucose.
   – Gluconeogenesis: formation of glucose from non-carbohydrate sources (glycerol plus amino acids)

2. The liver interacts with all the other systems of the body through its central role in processing and metabolizing nutrient-rich blood and dealing with waste products. The liver synthesizes molecules that are utilized elsewhere to support homeostasis, it converts molecules of one type to another, and it is central to regulating energy balances.

The Comparative Anatomy of the Heart (page 159)

1. Aorta: carry oxygenated blood to the head and body.

2. Vena cava: receives deoxygenated blood from the head and body.

3. An accessory air breathing organ provides more oxygen to the organism and also aids buoyancy.

4. Birds have lost the left side of the circulatory system, mammals have lost the right hand side.

5. This discussion will vary depending on the two vertebrates chosen as case studies. Some major points are described below:

Mammalian hearts: A double circuit system with a four chambered heart. The pulmonary circuit pumps blood through the right side of the heart to the lungs where the blood is oxygenated. The systemic circuit receives blood from the lungs and pumps blood through the left side of the heart to the body, where it supplies the tissues. An efficient system for animals with a high metabolic rate and high oxygen demand.
The heart in **birds** has the same circuitry as in mammals, i.e. a four chambered heart with fully separated pulmonary and systemic circuits.
Amphibians have a three chambered heart (two atria and a single ventricle), so there is mixing of oxygenated and deoxygenated blood. The sinus venosus (large in fish) is still a noticeable feature. Amphibians compensate for the single ventricle by supplementing oxygen uptake at the skin. **Reptile hearts** vary in the degree to which the ventricle is divided (it is functionally divided into two chambers in crocodilians), but in most there is some mixing of oxygenated and deoxygenated blood. Reptiles have a low metabolic rate and lower oxygen demand, relative to mammals, so this mixing presents no problem.
In **fish**, the heart is three/four chambered, with the chambers in series. There are no distinct pulmonary and systemic circuits; the blood flows from the heart at low pressure to the gills for oxygenation and then supplies the body before returning to the heart. Fish gills achieve high rates of oxygen extraction from the water, allowing these animals to achieve large sizes and rapid swimming speeds in spite of the lack of a discrete pulmonary circuit.

The Mammalian Heart (page 161)

1. Schematic of human heart. Labels (a)-(h)

   (a) Pulmonary artery   (e) Aorta
   (b) Vena cava   (f) Pulmonary vein
   (c) Right atrium   (g) Left atrium
   (d) Right ventricle   (h) Left ventricle

2. Valves prevent the blood from flowing the wrong way through the heart and help regulate filling of the chambers.

3. (a) The heart has its own coronary blood supply to meet the high oxygen demands of the heart tissue.
   (b) There must be a system within the heart muscle itself to return deoxygenated blood and waste products of metabolism back to the right atrium.

4. If blood flow to a particular part of the heart is restricted or blocked (because of blocked blood vessel), the part of the heart muscle supplied by that vessel will die, leading to a heart attack or infarction.

5. A: arterioles   B: venules
   C: arterioles   D: capillaries

6. (a) The pulmonary circuit must operate at a lower pressure than the systemic circuit to prevent fluid accumulation in the lungs. The systemic circuit must also develop enough pressure to enable blood flow to increase to the muscles when required and to maintain kidney filtration rates without compromising blood supply to the brain.
   (b) The left ventricle is thicker to enable the left side of the heart to develop higher pressure. There is no such requirement of the right side, which pumps

only to through the lower pressure pulmonary circuit.

7. You are recording expansion and recoil of the artery that occurs with each contraction of the left ventricle.

The Control of Heart Activity (page 163)

1. (a) **Sinoatrial node**: Initiates the cardiac cycle through the spontaneous generation of action potentials.
   (b) **Atrioventricular node**: Delays the impulse.
   (c) **Bundle of His**: Distributes the action potentials over the ventricles (resulting in ventricular contraction).
   (d) Electrical junctions allow action potentials to spread rapidly without delay.

2. Delaying the impulse at the AVN allows time for atrial contraction to finish before the ventricles contract.

3. It enables the heart to be able to contract more forcibly if an increased blood volume enters the heart, therefore increasing blood flow at times of need (e.g. exercise).

4. Influencing heart rate via the CNS allows the heart to deliver blood efficiently in response to demand (e.g. exercise, fight or flight).

Exercise and Blood Flow (page 164)

1. Answers for missing values are listed top to bottom:

	At rest	Exercise
	(% of total)	(% of total)
Heart	4.0	4.2
Lung	2.0	1.1
Kidneys	22.0	3.4
Liver	27.0	3.4
Muscle	15.0	70.2
Bone	5.0	1.4
Skin	6.0	10.7
Thyroid	1.0	0.3
Adrenals	0.5	0.1
Other	3.5	1.0

2. The heart beats faster and harder to increase the volume of blood pumped per beat and the number of beats per minute (increased blood flow).

3. (a) Blood flow increases approximately 3.5 times.
   (b) Working tissues require more oxygen and nutrients than can be delivered by a resting rate of blood flow. Therefore the rate of blood flow (delivery to the tissues) must increase during exercise.

4. (a) Thyroid and adrenal glands.
   (b) They are not involved in exercise and do not require an increased blood flow. However, they require their usual blood supply to be maintained.

5. (a) Skeletal muscles (increases 16.7X), skin (increases 6.3X), and heart (increases 3.7X).
   (b) These tissues and organs are all directly involved in the exercise process and need a greater rate of supply of oxygen and nutrients. Skeletal muscles move the body, the heart must pump a greater volume of blood at a greater rate and the skin must help cool the body to maintain core temperature.

6. Heart size increases because (like any muscle) it gets bigger with work. The larger size also means it pumps a greater volume of blood more efficiently.

7. Endurance athletes have a lower body weight.

8. With each stroke, the heart pumps a larger volume of blood. Less energy is expended in pumping the same volume of blood.

9. A lower resting heart rate means that for most of the time, the heart is not working as hard as in someone with a higher resting heart rate.

Adaptations to High Altitude (page 165)

1. (a) Less oxygen is available for metabolism so people become breathless and often dizzy. Associated effects are headache, nausea, fatigue, and coughing.
   (b) Altitude sickness or mountain sickness.

2. (a) Heart and breathing rates increase.
   (b) Increased breathing rate increases the rate at which new air is brought into the lungs (compensating for lower oxygen). Increased heart rate pumps blood more rapidly to tissues to improve oxygen delivery.

3. Indigenous highland populations have evolved different genetic mechanisms to cope with living at high altitude. The genealogy of these adaptations can be traced through population genetics studies and throw light on patterns of ancestry and dispersal.

Physiological Responses to Toxic Substances (page 166)

1. Pollutants may include:
   - CO: Headaches, respiratory damage
   - Fine particles (e.g. smoke, ash): Respiratory illness.
   - SO_2, NOx, O_3: Cardiovascular disease
   - Fertilizers/pesticides: Skin irritations, gastrointestinal illness and vomiting.
   - Radiation (mostly solar. Radioactive waste is much less common): Skin cancer (melanoma)
   - Heavy metals: Headaches. Nerve damage.

2. Social effects of pollutants include the disruption of relationships as affected people may require care from parents, children or partners. These people may not be able to work because of their care duties resulting in lost productivity to the economy. Health insurance or welfare in payouts may increase. Treating diseases caused by pollutants may cost countries hundreds and millions of dollars a year (e.g. $150 million to treat lung diseases in the USA).

KEY TERMS: Word Find (page 167)

```
A O O S I N O A T R I A L N O D E T Z K I J B E V
T O I L L S R C L O S E D K H V B W D J V I V K E
R H T I S S U E F L U I D S W X F V Q G Y K O E O
I I C V E I N L M M I R Y O P E N P R B P I R H J
U Q J T Q P G G Q Z S A H A W E B X A Y T U T L B
M X T S Y S T E M I C C I R C U L A T I O N E A L
S U R F A C E A R E A V O L U M E I A D A G D R O
X X P B R E S P I R A T O R Y P I G M E N T U T O
Z H E M O L Y M P H B U F F E R F B Y Y H M B E D
S I N G L E P H O G Y G N S A B U L K F L O W R M
K R S O Q M V F K Z O A Y N V E N T R I C L E Y J
W D H T Z U Z B J N V T A O C A P I L L A R Y D I
A T R I O V E N T R I C U L A R N O D E O Y G O O
U M C H E M O R E C E P T O R S G N A F W B R U R
F K D P U L M O N A R Y C I R C U L A T I O N B F
S T O X I C F L R R L M H E A R T Z L Y M P H L Q
B Y A V J G E Z U V B Y B L O O D V E S S E L E O
```

Answer list below given in the same order as the clues in the student workbook: artery, atrium, blood, chemoreceptors, blood vessel, capillary, hemolymph, heart, atrioventricular node, lymph, double, open, pulmonary circulation, toxic, buffer, surface area volume, systemic circulation, sinoatrial node, tissue fluid, vein, ventricle, single, respiratory pigment, closed.

Chemical Defenses in Animals (page 169)

1. (a) Having a number of different non-specific responses allows an organism to respond quickly to any pathogen. The organism can launch a fast defensive response to try and prevent the pathogen from spreading further.
   (b) (delete 'a' from question) Having only general immune responses means that an organism cannot produce a specific immune response to deal with a specific pathogen. There is no long-lasting or protective immunity developed (i.e. no immunological memory).

2. Vertebrates and non-vertebrates share many of the same non-specific defense mechanisms (e.g. lysozymes and antimicrobial peptides such as defensins). However, each also have features unique to them. Invertebrates have the ProPO system which initiates a melanization cascade to kill pathogens. Vertebrates produce an inflammatory response designed to limit the spread of pathogens.

Plant Defenses (page 170)

1. (a) Passive defenses: Physical or chemical barriers that are always present as part of the plant's normal make-up (not induced by contact with a pathogen).
   (b) Active defenses: Defenses invoked after physical attack or contact with a pathogen. They react specifically against the infection or damage.

2. Galls seal off the infected region with impenetrable tissue so the spread of the pathogen is limited.

3. Active defense mechanisms have similar properties to the immune response of animals, i.e. they are invoked after contact with the pathogen.

Targets for Defense (page 171)

1. The natural population of (normally non-pathogenic) microbes can benefit the host by preventing overgrowth of pathogens (through competitive exclusion).

2. (a) The MHC is a cluster of tightly linked genes on chromosome 6 in humans. The genes code for MHC antigens that are attached to the surfaces of all body cells and are used by the immune system to distinguish its own from foreign tissue.
   (b) This self-recognition system allows the body to immediately identify foreign tissue e.g. a pathogen, and mount an immune attack against it for the protection of the body's own tissues.

3. Self-recognition undesirable:
   - During pregnancy: **Note**: Some features of the self-recognition system are disabled to enable the growth (to term) of what is basically a foreign body.
   - During tissue and organ grafts and transplants from another human (allografts) or animal (xenografts).

Allergies and Hypersensitivity (page 172)

1. Histamine mediates the symptoms of hypersensitivity reactions such as inflammation, airway constriction, and itching and watering of the eyes and nose.

2. Being sensitized means to form antibodies to an antigen after exposure to it. Once sensitized, another exposure to the antigen results in an antibody-antigen reaction (and the symptoms of an allergic response).

3. Hypersensitivity is a malfunction of the immune system as it is reacting to particles that are harmless and do not require an immune response.

4. (a) Bronchodilators dilate the bronchioles.
   (b) By expanding the smaller airways, they alleviate airway constriction and allow easier breathing.

Our Body's Defenses (page 173)

1. **Specific resistance** refers to defense against particular (identified) pathogens. It involves a range of specific responses to the pathogen concerned (antibody production and cell-mediated immunity). In contrast, **non-specific resistance** refers to defense against any type of pathogen. it takes the form of physical and chemical barriers against infection, as well as phagocytosis and inflammation.

2. The skin provides a physical barrier to prevent entry of pathogens. Skin secretions (serum and sweat) contain antimicrobial chemicals which inhibit microbial growth.

3. (a) **Phospholipases** kill bacteria by hydrolyzing the phospholipids in cell walls and membranes.
   (b) **Cilia** move microbes, which are trapped in mucus, towards the mouth and nostrils, to be expelled.
   (c) **Sebum** has antimicrobial activity and (with sweat) a pH that is unfavorable for microbial growth.

4. (a) **Phagocytosis** destroys pathogens directly by engulfing them.
   (b) Antimicrobial substances (e.g. **interferon**) prevent multiplication of microbes (especially viruses).
   (c) Antibodies are produced against specific pathogens, and bind and destroy pathogens or their toxins.

5. A three tiered (hierarchical) system of defense provides a series of back-ups in case a pathogen breaches earlier barriers. Most microbes are excluded by the first line of defense, but those that penetrate the skin will usually be destroyed by white blood cells and the chemicals associated with inflammation. Failing this, the body will mount a targeted specific defense against the identified pathogen still remaining.

Blood Group Antigens (page 175)

1. Completed table:

Blood type	Antigen	Antibody	Can donate to:	Can receive blood from:
A	A	anti-B	A, AB	A, O
B	B	anti-A	B, AB	B, O
AB	A + B	none	AB	A, B, AB, O
O	None	anti-A + anti-B	O, AB, A, B	O

2. People with O- blood are often referred to as universal donors because they can donate blood to all other blood types (their red blood cells have no antigens).

3. Hemolytic disease of the newborn can occur when an Rh⁻ mother develops anti-Rh antibodies as a result of a first pregnancy with an Rh⁺ child. If a second child is also Rh⁺, these previously formed antibodies will cross the placenta, reacting with and destroying the red blood cells of the baby.

The Action of Phagocytes (page 176)

1. Neutrophils, eosinophils, macrophages.

2. By looking at the ratio of white blood cells to red blood cells (not involved in the immune response). An elevated white blood cell count (specifically a high neutrophil count) indicates microbial infection.

3. Microbes may be able to produce toxins that kill phagocytes directly. Others can enter the phagocytes, completely filling them and preventing them functioning or remaining dormant and resuming activity later.

Inflammation (page 177)

1. (a) Increased diameter and permeability of blood vessels. **Role**: Increases blood flow and delivery of leukocytes to the area. Aids removal of destroyed microbes or their toxins. Allows defensive substances to leak into the tissue spaces.
   (b) Phagocyte migration and phagocytosis. **Role**: To directly attack and destroy invading microbes and foreign substances.
   (c) Tissue repair. **Role**: Replaces damaged cells and tissues, restoring the integrity of the area.

2. Ability to squeeze through capillary walls (amoeboid movement). Ability to engulf material by phagocytosis.

3. Histamines and prostaglandins attract phagocytes to the site of infection.

4. Pus is the accumulated debris of infection (dead phagocytes, damaged tissue, and fluid). It accumulates at the infection site where the defense process is active.

The Lymphathic System (page 178)

1. **Lymph** has a similar composition to tissue fluid but has more leukocytes (derived from lymphoid tissues). **Note**: Tissue fluid is similar in composition to plasma (i.e. containing water, ions, urea, proteins, glucose etc.) but lacks the large proteins found in plasma.

2. Lymph returns tissue fluid to general circulation, and with the blood, circulates lymphocytes around the body.

3. (a) **Lymph nodes**: Filter foreign material from the lymph by trapping it in fibers. They also produce lymphocytes.
   (b) **Bone marrow**: Produce many kinds of white blood cells: monocytes, macrophages, neutrophils, eosinophils, basophils, T and B lymphocytes.

Acquired Immunity (page 179)

1. (a) **Passive immunity** describes the immunity that develops after antibodies are transferred from one

person to another. In this case, the recipient does not make the antibodies themselves.

(b) **Naturally acquired** passive immunity arises as a result of antibodies passing from the mother to the foetus/infant via the placenta/breast milk. **Artificially acquired** passive immunity arises as a result of injection with immune serums e.g. in antivenoms.

2. (a) Newborns need to be supplied with maternal antibodies because they have not yet had exposure to the everyday microbes in their environment and must be born with operational defense mechanisms.

(b) The antibody "supply" is (ideally) supplemented with antibodies in breast milk because it takes time for the infant's immune system to become fully functional. During this time, the supply of antibodies received during pregnancy will decline.

(c) Yes. Breast feeding will provide the infant with a naturally acquired passive immunity to help protect it against infections while its immune system develops. Without this acquisition, the infant is more vulnerable to everyday infections against which you already have immunity but he/she does not.

3. (a) **Active immunity** is immunity that develops after the body has been exposed to a microbe or its toxins and an immune response has been invoked.

(b) **Naturally acquired** active immunity arises as a result of exposure to an antigen such as a pathogen, e.g. natural immunity to chickenpox. **Artificially acquired** active immunity arises as a result of vaccination, e.g. any childhood disease for which vaccinations are given: diphtheria, measles, mumps, polio etc.

4. (a) The primary response is less pronounced (smaller magnitude) than the secondary response. The primary response takes longer to develop and is over more quickly than the secondary response, which is rapid and long lasting.

(b) The immune system has already been "primed" or prepared to respond to the antigen by the first exposure to it. When the cells of the immune system receive a second exposure to the same antigen they can respond quickly with rapid production of antibodies.

5. (a) Herd immunity refers to the protection that unimmunized people have against a circulating disease by virtue of the fact that most of the population are immunized.

(b) A fall in vaccination rates is a concern because, once the population contains a high proportion of non-vaccinated people, herd immunity is lost and a circulating disease can spread very rapidly through the community, raising public health costs and contributing to lost productivity.

Vaccines and Vaccination (page 181)

1. **Attenuated viruses** are more effective in the long term because they tend to replicate in the body, and the original dose therefore increases over time. Such vaccines are derived from mutations accumulated over time in a laboratory culture, so there is always a risk that they will back-mutate to a virulent form.

2. High vaccination rates increase the rates of immunity within a population, so fewer people will contract the disease with each outbreak. Transmission of the disease is limited because there are fewer susceptible

hosts for the disease to exploit, until eventually the disease no longer occurs in the population.

3. (a) Introducing the whooping cough vaccine in the 1940s greatly reduced the number of cases of whooping cough contracted each year in the US.

(b) Whooping cough immunization rates may have dropped to public perception that the vaccine was unsafe and could cause side effects such as autism.

(c) Initially, the lower vaccination rate resulted in more cases of whooping cough. The number of whooping cough cases dropped steadily between 2005-2007, before beginning to increase again in 2008.

(d) Herd immunity will initially provide some protection, but as overall herd immunity drops (due to decreased vaccination rates) the cases of whooping cough will begin to increase.

4. Acellular vaccines contain only fragments of the pathogen, so they are less likely to be reactive and will cause fewer side effects than whole agent vaccines. Acellular vaccines are still highly effective.

The Immune System (page 183)

1. (a) **Humoral immune system**: Production of antibodies against specific antigens. The antibodies disable circulating antigens.

(b) **Cell-mediated immune system**: Involves the production of T cells, which destroy pathogens or their toxins by direct contact or by producing substances that regulate the activity of other cells in the immune system.

2. In the bone marrow (adults) or liver (fetuses).

3. (a) Bone marrow   (b) Thymus

4. (a) **Memory cells**: Retain an antigen memory. They can rapidly differentiate into antibody-producing plasma cells if they encounter the same antigen again.

(b) **Plasma cells**: Secrete antibodies against antigens (very rapid rate of antibody production).

(c) **Helper T cells**: Activate cytotoxic T cells and other helper T cells. Also needed for B cell activation.

(d) **Suppressor T cells**: Regulate the immune system response by turning it off when antigens disappear.

(e) **Delayed hypersensitivity T cells**: Cause inflammation in allergic responses and are responsible for rejection of transplanted tissue.

(f) **Cytotoxic T cells**: Destroy target cells on contact (by binding and lysing cells).

5. **Immunological memory**: The result of the differentiation of B cells after the first exposure to an antigen. Those B cells that differentiate into long lived memory cells are present to react quickly and vigorously in the event of a second infection.

Antibodies (page 185)

1. **Antibodies** are proteins produced in response to antigens; they recognize and bind antigens. **Antigens** are foreign substances (often proteins) that promote the formation of antibodies (invoke an immune response).

2. Antibodies consist of two heavy (long) peptide chains each attached to a light (short) peptide chain, commonly forming a Y configuration. The variable

region at the ends of the heavy and light chains form the antigen binding sites.

3. (a) The immune system must distinguish self from non-self in order to recognize foreign material (and destroy it) and its own tissue (and not destroy it).
   (b) During development, any B cells that react to the body's own antigens are selectively destroyed. This process leads to **self tolerance**.
   (c) Autoimmune disease (disorder).
   (d) Any two of: Grave's disease (thyroid enlargement), rheumatoid arthritis (primarily joint inflammation), insulin-dependent diabetes mellitus (caused by immune destruction of the insulin-secreting cells in the pancreas), hemolytic anemia (premature destruction of red blood cells), and probably multiple sclerosis (destruction of myelin around nerves).

4. Antibodies inactivate pathogens in four main ways: **Neutralization** describes the way in which antibodies bind to viral binding sites and bacterial toxins and stop their activity. Antibodies may also **inactivate particulate antigens**, such as bacteria, by sticking them together in clumps. Soluble antigens may be bound by antibodies and fall out of solution (**precipitation**) so that they lose activity. Antibodies also activate **complement** (a defense system involving serum proteins), tagging foreign cells so that they can be recognized and destroyed.

5. (a) **Phagocytosis**: Antibodies promote the formation of inactive clumps of foreign material that can easily be engulfed and destroyed by a phagocytic cell.
   (b) **Inflammation**: Antibodies are involved in activation of complement (the defense system involving serum proteins which participate in the inflammatory response and other immune system activities).
   (c) **Bacterial cell lysis**: Antibodies are involved in tagging foreign cells for destruction and in the activation of complement (the defense system involving serum proteins which participate in the lysis of foreign cells).

Monoclonal Antibodies (page 187)

1. (a) B-lymphocyte cells.
   (b) The immune system of some people reacts against the foreign (mouse) proteins (antibodies).

2. Tumor cells are immortal and can be cultured indefinitely.

3. (a)-(d) in any order:
   (a) Diagnostic tool for detecting pathogens.
   (b) Diagnostic tool for detecting pregnancy hormones.
   (c) Neutralizing endotoxins in blood infections.
   (d) Interfering with T cell activity responsible for transplant rejection.

4. (a) Detection of bacteria or toxins in perishable food would allow the food to be disposed of rather than consumed and hence the possibility of food poisoning avoided.
   (b) Detection of pregnancy at home would give an instant result, and may circumvent a costly visit to a doctor until a pregnancy was confirmed. For some people, pregnancy detection in the privacy of their home is an attractive option.
   (c) Targeted treatment of cancerous tumors could avoid the need for more invasive or aggressive

conventional cancer therapies (which have numerous, often distressing side effects).

AIDS: Failures of Defense (page 189)

1. HIV attacks the system that normally defends the body from infection. By knocking out the immune system, it leaves the body vulnerable to invasion by microbes that would not normally infect a healthy person.

2. (a) The virus rapidly increases in numbers within the first year of infection, followed by a large drop off in numbers in the second year. Over the next 3-10 years, the HIV population gradually increases again.
   (b) The helper T cell numbers respond to the initial infection by increasing in numbers. After about a year, their numbers steadily decrease as they are attacked and destroyed by the HIV.

KEY TERMS: Word Find (page 190)

Answer list below given in the same order as the clues in the student workbook: active immunity, macrophage, humoral, antibody, immunological memory, AIDS, immune response, antigen, B cell, cell mediated, inflammation, clonal selection, lymphocyte, disease, HIV, monoclonal, immunity, leukocyte, infection, MHC, non-specific defense, passive, pathogen. **Erratum**: *words for which there were no clues: phagocyte, primary response, secondary response, specific defense, T cell, thymus, vaccination. Clues for these will be provided as an erratum from the weblinks page and in the Teacher's Guide. Our apologies.*

Timing and Coordination in Simple Organisms (page 192)

1. (a) Acyl homoserine lactones (AHLs) are produced by *P. aeruginosa*. When the concentration reaches a critical level, virulence genes are expressed and toxins are produced.
   (b) When resources are low, *M. xanthus* cells begin to starve. This triggers the production of factor A. When factor A concentrations are high enough, *M. xanthus* cells congregate to form a fruiting body.

2. Production of toxins by *P. aeruginosa* will kill off other organisms and enable it to have a larger share of the resources available. The formation of fruiting bodies by *M. xanthus* cells results in the formation of spores able to withstand the lack of resources. Spores are transported to other areas where they will germinate and exploit the resources available there.

Plant Responses (page 193)

1. Light (including the light/dark cycle), gravity, temperature, touch, chemicals.

2. Appropriate responses enhance survival in different environments. Appropriate responses to environmental stimuli enable the plant to synchronize its daily cycles and seasonally important events, such as germination, with environmental cues.

3. (a) Closing of stomata
   (b) Leaf fall, dormancy
   (c) Closing of stomata, leaf closure (nastic response) in some plants.
   (d) Leaf closure (nastic response).
   (e) Closing of flowers.

Tropisms and Growth Responses (page 194)

1. (a) Positive chemotropism
   (b) Negative gravitropism
   (c) Positive hydrotropism
   (d) Positive phototropism
   (e) Positive gravitropism
   (f) Positive thigmomorphogenesis (*alt.* thigmotropism)

2. A **tropism** is a growth response to an environmental stimulus, where the direction of the growth response is determined by stimulus direction. A **nastic response**, unlike a tropism, is independent of the stimulus direction. Nasties are usually quite rapid, often reversible movements. Tropisms are usually slower growth responses.

3. (a) Enables roots to turn and grow down into the soil (where they obtain moisture and nutrients).
   (b) Enables coleoptiles to turn up and grow towards the sunlight (necessary for food manufacture).
   (c) Enables the plant to clamber upwards and grow toward the light instead of possibly becoming smothered by more upright plants.
   (d) Enables pollen tube to locate the micropyle of the embryo sac, and sperm nuclei to fertilize the egg.

Investigating Phototropism (page 195)

1. (a) Hormone: auxin.
   (b) Response: positive phototropism.
   (c) **Point A**: Cells stay short.   **Point B**: Cells elongate.
   (d) Side B

   (e)
   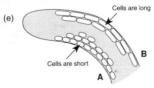
   Cells are long

   Cells are short

   B

   A

2. The hormone is produced in the shoot tip. The light initiates the response.

3. **Plant A**: The plant will exhibit phototropism and bend towards the sun. **Plant B**: The plant will exhibit no phototropic behavior and will not bend.

Investigating Gravitropism (page 196)

1. (a) In shoots, more auxin accumulates on the lower side of the shoot. In response to higher auxin levels here, the cells on the lower side of the stem elongate and the shoot tip turns up.
   (b) In roots, the accumulation of auxin on the lower side inhibits elongation (since this is the response of roots to high auxin). The cells on the upper side therefore elongate more than those on the lower side and the root tip turns down.

2. (a) Approximately 10^{-3} mg l^{-1}
   (b) Stem growth is promoted.

3. (a) Stems: A negative geotropic response ensures shoots turn up towards the light (important when light may be absent as when buried deeply in soil).
   (b) Roots: Positive geotropism ensures roots turn down into the soil so that they can begin obtaining the water and minerals required for continued growth.

Nastic Responses (page 197)

1. Possible advantages:
   – Closing the leaf makes it less attractive to grazers (especially if thorns are exposed), and less of the plant is likely to be eaten.
   – Drooping of the plant exposes less leaf surface area for evaporative loss of water during windy periods.

2. Disturbance to the leaflets is transmitted as a surface membrane potential to the cells at the base of the leaflets (pulvini). In response to the change in membrane potential, potassium ions are pumped out of the cytoplasm of the cells. Water follows osmotically, causing a sudden loss of turgor in the cells supporting the leaf(let) bases. **Note**: In the leaflets, turgor loss occurs on the upper surface of the pulvinus (leaflet folds up). In the entire leaf, turgor loss occurs on the lower surface of the pulvinus (leaf droops down).

3. During daylight, the leaves are maximally spread for light capture. At night the leaves fold down. There is no light capture and water is conserved by a lowered leaf.

Photoperiodism (page 198)

1. Light induced responses involving phytochrome; (a) and (b) any two of: Seed germination, leaf growth, flowering (long day plants), chlorophyll synthesis.

2. Phytochrome is a photosensitive pigment which changes from the inactive form to the active form on absorption of light. The plant measures daylength by the amount of phytochrome of each form present.

3. (a) Day length (perhaps more importantly, night length).
   (b) Any one of:
   – Flowering at the same time ensures that other flowers will be available to provide/receive pollen.
   – Synchronization with periods of high insect activity may assist pollination.

4. Environmental cues for triggering and breaking dormancy include: decreasing day length (short days); long, cold nights; dry, nitrogen deficient soils. The necessity of exposure to cold to break dormancy ensures the plant does not "mistake" transient environmental cues.

5. **Dormancy** is a condition of arrested growth and metabolism and occurs when conditions for plant growth and survival are poor (such as occurs in the winters of temperate regions). Dormancy allows survival over the inclement period. **Vernalization** refers to the low temperature stimulation of flowering. For plants in temperate regions, this is adaptive because, after a relatively long period of intense cold, a period of warmth indicates that the winter has passed and the new growing period has begun.

6. (a) Short-day plants: Flower only when the day length is short (average: 10 hours).
   (b) Long-day plants: Flower only when the day length exceeds a certain minimum value (average: 14 h).

7. Short-day plants are really long night plants, requiring a night length of more than a minimum value. In the experiment outlined, a short-day plant failed to flower when a long night was interrupted by a short period of light (the plant interpreted this as a short night irrespective of the short day prior to it).

Plant Hormones and Timing Responses
(page 200)

1. Both processes result in either leaf or fruit falling from the tree. It could therefore be assumed that both process were similar, and would involve interactions between the same hormones (auxin and ethylene).

2. **Gibberellins** are strong promoters of elongation in stems by stimulating both cell division and cell elongation. In seeds, gibberellins are responsible for breaking dormancy and stimulating the growth of the embryo and emergence of the seedling.

3. If picked ripe, the fruit would arrive at its destination overripe. Artificial ripening allows fruit to be delivered to market in an optimal state.

Biological Rhythms (page 201)

1. (a) **Daily**: Approximates the cycle of a solar day (period = 24 h). The rhythm persists in darkness.
   Example: Body temperature fluctuations in humans.
   (b) **Lunar**: Approximates the cycle of a lunar month (period = 29.5 days).
   Example: Menstrual cycle in women.
   (c) **Annual**: Approximates the cycle of a solar year (period = 365.25 days).
   Example: Hibernation in bears through the northern hemisphere winter.
   (d) **Tidal**: Approximates the cycle of a tidal cycle (period = 12.35).
   Example: Barnacles opening (to feed) and closing (to avoid desiccation) with incoming and outgoing tides respectively.

2. (a) Hedgehog's hibernation: When mean earth temperatures drop to 10-11°C.
   (b) Blackbird's foraging: Sunrise and sunset (light: dark cycle).
   (c) Screech Owl's activity: Sunrise and sunset (light: dark cycle).
   (d) Spring flowering: Change in day length.

3. An **exogenous rhythm** is a rhythm that occurs in direct response to an environmental stimulus external to the

organism. An example is the is the hopping of sparrows on a perch when a light is turned on. **Note**: Truly exogenous rhythms are rare. Most rhythms have both an endogenous and exogenous component.

Biological Clocks (page 202)

1. Activities requiring preparation:
   – Birth of young: Requires nest building & acquisition of food resources (e.g. most birds, many mammals).
   – Migration: Forming herds, flocks etc. for mass migrations (e.g. many migratory birds, large herd mammals of the African savannah).
   – Hibernation and dormancy: Consumption of extra food to put on weight, preparation of a den or movement to a hideaway (e.g. some bears, some small marsupials, some desert-dwelling frogs).

2. (a) A zeitgeber resets the internal biological clock.
   (b) Common zeitgeber is the light-dark cycle.

3. Many international travelers suffer jet lag when they reach their destination. Melatonin is a hormone associated with regulating sleep-wake cycles and produced only in the dark. By taking melatonin when they reach their destination, travelers can sleep and also reset their biological clock to the new time zone.

Human Biorhythms (page 203)

1. (a) White blood cell count:
Daily:	10-11 pm
Monthly:	At the end of the menstrual cycle
Annually:	May/June
   (b) Body temperature:
Daily:	5-6 pm
Monthly:	Last quarter of menstrual cycle
Annually:	December

2. A- The data on deaths relate only to those by natural causes. Fewer deaths occur at the time of greatest body temperature. More deaths occur between midnight and noon, when body temperature is lower.

3. (a) 1-2 pm
   (b) Peak brain activity and memory responses occur at this time. Speed in addition peaks at 4 pm.

4. (a) 5 pm
   (b) Insulin is a hormone responsible for cellular uptake of glucose and for converting glucose to glycogen. The main meal for the day is at about 5 pm. Insulin peaks then so that the glucose released into the blood after eating can be utilised.

5. After midnight (worst at about 7 am).

6. Peaks during the coldest time of the year (cold conditions may stimulate hair growth).

7. (a) Daily fluctuations in body temperature.
   (b) Line of best fit:

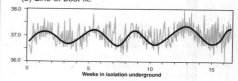

(c) Menstrual cycle (monthly rhythm).
(d) To exclude as many environmental cues as possible (e.g. day night cycle) so that she would not reset her biorhythms. Even subtle stimuli, such as distant noise levels and smells, may act as cues.

Recording Animal Activity (page 205)

1. (a) 23.5 hours   (b) A- 24.5 hours

2. Circadian (approximating to a 24 hour period).

3. (a) The periods of the rhythms are different.
   (b) A is more regular and less broken than B.

4. (a) 13 hours
   (b) Circatidal (period of ~12.5 hours, with tidal flows).
   (c) None in the lab (it is free-running).
   (d) Anticipates incoming tides to begin foraging activity, and the outgoing tides to bury into the sand and so avoid desiccation.
   (e) To remove any possible effect of temperature changes on behavior.
   (f) Tidal cycle of high and low tides.

Rhythms in Cockroaches (page 206)

1. Daily rhythm with nocturnal activity. Note that if the evidence from days 11-20 is also taken into account it is also acceptable to identify this as a circadian rhythm (the rhythm persists in the absence of cues).

2. Immediately after the onset of darkness.

3. Cockroaches are nocturnal.

4. Approximately 24.5 hours.

5. **Entrainment** refers to the synchronisation of a free-running endogenous rhythm with an exogenous cue, such as the light-dark cycle. Most endogenous rhythms have a free-running period that is slightly more or less than the environmental cycle (its zeitgeber). Entrainment keeps the organism's activity pattern in keeping with an appropriate environmental cue; without entrainment, the endogenous rhythm will tend to drift.

Hibernation (page 207)

1. (a) Hibernation is a prolonged state of reduced metabolic activity and reduced body temperature.
   (b) It allows animals to conserve energy at times when food is scarce. If they didn't hibernate the animal would spend large amounts of time and energy trying to find food. If not enough food was available (as in winter), they re likely to die.
   (c) Common cues include shortage of food, shorter daylight periods, and decreased environmental temperature.
   (d) Facultative hibernators can be aroused by external cues during hibernation. The process involved in arousal, and going back into hibernation cost energy. If it occurs too often, energy expenditure can be high.

2. (a) Their body temperature drops about 30°C during hibernation
   (b) It slows down metabolism. Less energy is consumed, so the animal can survive off its reserves and does not need to wake to forage.
   (c) The elevated metabolic rate allows the animal to wake from hibernation more quickly. It also clears the body of any toxins or waste products that may have built up over the hibernation period.

The Components of Behavior (page 208)

1. **Innate** behavior has a genetic basis: It is present from birth and does not need to be learned. **Learned** behavior results from the experiences of the animal, i.e. existing behaviors are modified as a result of experiences (may be imprinting, conditioning, habituation, imitation, or higher level cognition).

2. (a) A releaser triggers the operation of the innate behavioral program that results in the predictable, stereotyped behavioral response (the FAP).
   (b) Many examples are possible, including those we may have all observed in domestic pets (opening car door = barking, opening refrigerator = meowing). The most striking FAPs are those that occur when animals interact with conspecifics in courtship, territory defense, or dominance encounters. The releaser and the FAP form a signaling system; signaling is the primary purpose of such behaviors. Good illustrative examples include:
   - Red belly models (releaser) in three-spined sticklebacks eliciting the attack response (the FAP) in male sticklebacks.
   - Speckling and (green) color (releaser) eliciting egg rolling behavior (the FAP) in herring gulls.
   - Bill shape and red patch (releaser) eliciting pecking behavior (the FAP) in herring gull chicks.

Simple Behaviors (page 209)

1. A **kinesis** describes movement of a cell or organism in which the rate of movement depends upon the intensity (rather than direction) of the stimulus. An example is the increased activity of body lice when temperature increases over 30°C. In contrast, a **taxis** is a directional movement in response to an external stimulus. An example is the negative phototaxis of maggots.

2. Such simple behaviors allow an animal to continue making random orientation responses until it is in an environment that is favorable to its survival (e.g. body lice must reach an appropriate host, as indicated by the surface skin temperature). Once positioned, the behavior will cease until environmental conditions change once again.

3. (a) Gravi –   Gravity
   (b) Hydro –   Water/moisture/humidity
   (c) Thigmo –   Touch
   (d) Photo –   Light
   (e) Chemo –   Chemical
   (f) Thermo –   Heat

4. (a) A Snails: Negative gravitaxis
   (b) B Moth: Positive chemotaxis
   (c) C Louse: Kinesis in response to temperature
   (d) D Lobster: Positive thigmotaxis
   (e) E Mosquitoes: Positive thermotaxis
   (f) F Maggots: Negative phototaxis

5. 30°C

Migration Patterns (page 210)

1. Nomadic migration might be necessary to escape deteriorating habitats and colonize new ones (perhaps where there are more suitable breeding sites). For example, humans following seasonal food sources.

2. One-way migration (dispersal) and nomadic migrations.

3. Any of a number of examples: Change in temperature, or day length, or change in food supply (reduced).

4. Migration is adaptive in that it allows individuals to relocate to an area more suited to their survival at a certain life stage (i.e. more favorable with better food resources and/or breeding sites and/or climate).

Animal Migrations (page 211)

1. (a) Migratory locust: 7   (f) Monarch butterfly: 2
   (b) Caribou: 3   (g) European swift: 6
   (c) Shearwater: 9   (h) Humpback whale: 1
   (d) Polar bear: 8   (i) European eels: 4
   (e) Green turtle: 5   (j) Spiny lobster: 10

2. (a) **Migratory locust**: Dispersal away from depleted food supply to new areas rich in food.
   (b) **Monarch butterfly**: To avoid climatic extremes; moving away from harsh northern winter temperatures, followed by movement away from Mexico's summer heat.
   (c) **Humpback whale**: Exploiting the plankton-rich summer feeding grounds in the polar regions; enhancing survival of newborn in winter breeding grounds in the tropics (possibly because it is desirable for young to be born in shallow and sheltered waters).
   (d) **Spiny lobster**: Compensation for gradual loss of population "downstream" of the longshore current.

3. (a) Takes a huge physiological toll (uses up energy).
   (b) Exposes animal to new dangers (predators etc.)

4. (a) Continental drift: As land masses have moved apart gradually (a few centimeters a year) any habitual movement over a short distance (sea or land) may become a long distance migration if the animals keep to their original starting points and destinations.
   (b) Ice ages: The expansion and contraction of ice sheets forced many animal populations to change their global distribution. Birds in particular would find their habitats alternately shrinking and expanding.

Migratory Navigation in Birds (page 213)

1. **European starlings** show that innate behavior programmes are involved in the movement of the birds in a certain direction (young birds fly southwest). Experienced birds can modify their innate behavior and learn to correct deviations from their flight path. **Blackcaps** show their sense of direction is genetically determined, as hybrids fly a course that is intermediate between W and E populations.

2. (a) Sun compass: The fact that the birds were in natural conditions (suggesting all other variables were held constant) and that they consistently orientated with respect to the direction of incoming light clearly supports the sun compass hypothesis. Note that this was demonstrated with more than one bird.
   (b) Magnetic compass: The birds realigned their position to what they sensed to be the magnetic north. The fact that it took 3 days is interesting but not important.
   (c) Star compass: When the planetarium 'sky' was rotated 90°, the birds altered their orientation to compensate. No visible sky resulted in confused, apparently random responses. A star compass seems highly probable.

3. Birds using a **sun compass** must have a biological clock of some kind to calibrate the sun's movement to time of day (to allow for the sun's changing position).

Homing in Insects (page 215)

1. (a) Honey bee: sun compass.
   (b) Moth: pheromone (airborne scent) trail.
   (c) Digger wasp: visual landmarks.
   (d) Ant: chemical trail.
   (e) Mosquito: heat and carbon dioxide gradient.

2. **Homing** refers to the return of an animal to a home base (e.g. nest, hive) or place of birth after a period of absence (e.g. foraging). This differs from animal **migration** where animals undergo a change of habitat according to a change in season, climate, or resources. Animal migration often occurs over very long distances and along predetermined routes.

Learned Behavior (page 216)

1. Filial imprinting results in a social attachment for conspecifics (usually kin). It is adaptive in that it promotes survival behavior (e.g. following) early in life and ensures that subsequent social behaviors will be directed appropriately to members of the same species.

2. Habituation is adaptive because it prevents continued responses to stimuli that provide no reinforcement (reward or punishment). This (1) prevents sensory overload and (2) enables animals to respond to the stimuli that are associated with a consequence.

3. Latent learning is critical to survival where it is associated with behaviors such as navigation and homing, or acquisition of food. Such behavior enables an animal to correctly locate certain resources based on the total configuration of landmarks in the environment, e.g. location of food caches in squirrels and nutcracker birds. Cooperative hunting in pack carnivores, such as hunting dogs, probably also includes some elements of latent learning.

4. (a) Operant conditioning describes the situation where an animal learns to associate a particular behavior with a reward.
   (b) Animals exploring their environment will naturally trigger certain events by their actions. When the same action repeatedly triggers the same event, animals will very quickly learn to avoid or continue the behavior in accordance to its consequence.

5. Insight learning is difficult to test because the subject must not have been exposed to a similar problem before testing and the test can not be repeated on the same individual (as this would then involve experience or learning by trial and error). Care must also be taken to make sure other potential subjects do not see the first subject attempting or completing the task.

Learning to Sing (page 218)

1. (a) In white-crowned sparrows, birds older than 4 months are no longer receptive to further modification of the song.
   (b) Birds deafened as juveniles, even after being exposed to adult song, cannot produce a normal song (only a variable call with no phrasing).
   (c) Birds are capable of producing a simple but phrased song (which is never-the-less recognizably that of a white-crowned sparrow) even when isolated or exposed to the songs of other species during the period of song development. This shows that a certain component of the species song is innate. Young birds exposed to the song of conspecifics during the song development period then learn to modify this basic pattern to sing a fully phrased normal adult song.

2. The ability to modify an innate song pattern by learning has consequences for an individual in terms of attracting a mate over rivals. In evolutionary terms, birds more capable of attracting mates because they can modify and develop a song pattern will pass on this aspect of fitness to their offspring and their genes will have greater representation in later generations.

Animal Communication (page 219)

1. (a) Ritualization of signals makes the message easily understood and unlikely to be misinterpreted.
   (b) Communication over long distances may communicate information about location, sexual receptiveness or territory and so either attract others or warn them off. Communication over short distances may convey similar information or it may contain information about status, and so help keep social order, as in a hierarchy.

2. Communication methods best suited to nocturnal activity in forest include vocalization (e.g. as in frogs) and olfaction. Visual communication is difficult or impossible (especially color) when there is no light.

3. The physiological changes prepare the body for the extra work it might have to do in either flighting off the threat or fleeing from it. The increased breathing rate, heart rate, and muscular activity prepares the body to most efficiently flee or defend itself.

Social Organization (page 221)

1. (a) Genetically, through behavior that is innate.
   (b) Learning, by observation and imitation.

2. (a) Richer learning environment: Provides more opportunities to observe a diverse range of behaviors. A larger group may provide better opportunity to find a 'teacher'.
   (b) Division of labor among specialists: Some animal species have morphologically different specialists, adapted to perform specific tasks (e.g. termites have workers, soldiers, kings, and queens). Other species have different behaviors (e.g. members of a meerkat group may be assigned specific tasks such as guarding or nursery care). By specializing in a particular set of behaviors, animals in a group can achieve greater efficiencies as a whole.
   (c) Assembly for mate selection: Allows animals that are highly mobile/nomadic/widely dispersed to find a mate. This increases mate choice/selection.

3. (a) Line of best fit:

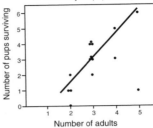

The effect of number of adults in the family on pup survival

Number of pups surviving (y-axis)
Number of adults (x-axis)

There appears to be a direct positive linear relationship between the number of adult helpers and pup survival.
   (b) Helpers may assist by (any two of):
   – regurgitating food for the mother
   – regurgitating food for the pups
   – helping to hunt cooperatively
   – helping to defend territory (also against predators)

4. Beneficial social behavior may become more common in a species if it increases survival of offspring that have inherited the behavioral trait of cooperation, or have learned to cooperate and are likely to pass on the behavior (through learning) to their own offspring.

Behavior and Species Recognition (page 223)

1. (a) **Courtship** behavior is a means of assessing the suitability, quality, and readiness of a mate and an effective way of ensuring reproductive isolation. It also has a role in reducing natural intraspecific aggression in the potential mate.
   (b) Stereotypical behaviors are easily recognized and will elicit appropriate (and equally recognizable) behaviors in the prospective mate.

2. Effective courtship provides a way to ensure that species do not mistakenly waste resources by mating with another species. This helps to ensure the production of viable offspring and maintains the integrity of the species gene pool.

Breeding Behavior (page 224)

1. (a) and (b) any two of the following in any order:
   – A display that allows mates to recognize each other and facilitate acceptance of the male by the female.
   – Lock and key genitalia to ensure sperm survival.
   – A cocooned gift presented by the male that keeps the female occupied during mating and ensures she has a good meal that will help egg production.

2. Responding to the appropriate photoperiod allows animals to produce eggs or young to coincide with the onset of better weather and food supplies.

3. Territory is important for reproductive success both for males and females. Males with superior territories are likely to attract more mates that others and so increase their chances of reproductive success. Females that

either have superior territory or move into the territory of a superior male are likely to have better resources during pregnancy and while feeding the offspring.

Pheromones (page 225)

1. (a) **Hormones** are chemicals produced by an animal in endocrine tissue and released into the bloodstream where they influence the physiology of target tissues **within the body**. In contrast, **pheromones** are chemicals produced by an animal and released into **the environment** where they influence the behavior or physiology of other individuals of the same species, e.g. as a sexual attractant.
    (b) Pheromones are species specific so that the message is received by 'the right organism', e.g. to attract a mate and trigger specific courtship behaviors, or to guide other individuals to food.

2. Roles of pheromones (a-c any three of):
    *   As mate attractants, e.g. moths.
    *   In chemical trails to locate food sources, e.g. ants.
    *   As an alarm to warn of danger, e.g. ants.
    *   To maintain social order, e.g. honeybee colonies.
    *   To chemically sample the environment, e.g. mammals and reptiles.

3. A pheromone trap (baited with a synthetic pheromone) would attract the male insect pests (females release the sex attractant) and contain them for later disposal. The fewer males remaining to breed would help decrease the overall size of the pest population.

Honeybee Communication (page 226)

1. Position of the sun during the day.

2. Bee communicates the proximity of the food source by the speed or intensity of the waggle of its abdomen.

3. The bee must compensate for the change in the position of the Sun. The bee will have to alter the angle of the dance with respect to the vertical reference of the comb.

4. The round dance is used for communicating about food sources that are very close (within 50 m of hive).

Cooperation and Survival (page 227)

1. **Altruistic behavior** refers to behavior where an animal performs a service for another at some cost to itself (e.g. an individual giving the alarm for an approaching predator might risk being targeted by the predator itself). Examples of true altruism are rare, and difficult to conclusively demonstrate or explain in evolutionary terms. Usually, there is some benefit to the altruistic individual, however tenuous. In contrast, **kin selection** refers to selection favoring altruistic behavior towards close relatives. For example, there is a selective advantage in pre-adult helpers assisting in rearing siblings as the chicks are related to them (kin).

2. The altruistic individual is helping to ensure the survival of relatives with whom it shares alleles in common. For some individuals, it is better to do this than to undertake the risky task of reproducing themselves (e.g., if resources are very limited or if better protection results from greater vigilance by kin).

3. When animals work together cooperatively, both the individual survival and population survival improves. Acquiring food, rearing young, and defense against predators are all enhanced by group cooperation, increasing survival of individuals. As a result, the population benefits (through better reproductive success), and population survival is enhanced.

Cooperative Defense and Attack (page 228)

1. (a) Musk oxen: Increased survival of young.
    (b) Army ants: They can overpower animals larger than would be possible by one individual. Cooperation enables dismembering and transport of food back to bivouac (temporary nest).

2. (a) As a form of group defense. Many eyes are able to detect an approaching predator. The movement of the mob of sheep during a predator's chase serves to confuse the predator.
    (b) Less time is spent keeping a lookout for predators, so that more time can be spent feeding.

Cooperative Food Gathering (page 229)

1. When individuals work together, the success rate increases. Individuals expend less energy obtaining food than they would if they foraged individually. Generally, survival rates improve. Because more food is obtained when individuals work together, there is enough food for all members of the group. Reproduction is more likely because there is enough food to sustain young, so the population will grow in size.

2. Having specific roles in food gathering increases the chances of obtaining food, so survival rates of individuals, and the population are higher. Some examples include:
    – Honeypot ants: food can be stored in repletes at times of abundance. When food is scarce food stored in the repletes is used by the colony until other food becomes available again.
    – Lions have specific roles during hunting to increase their success rate. Some lions drive prey towards other waiting in ambush downwind. When the prey gets close enough, the lions waiting in ambush attack. All the lions can then share the kill, so all benefit.

KEY TERMS: Mix and Match (page 230)

abscisic acid (Q), auxin (G), cooperative behavior (I), courtship (X), environmental cue (B), ethylene (S), gravitropism (C), hibernation (P), homing (N), innate behavior (E), insight (A), kinesis (F), learned behavior (W), magnetic compass (Y), migration (H), nastic response (R), navigation (D), operant learning (K), pheromone (V), photoperiodism (M), phototropism (O), social behavior (L), sun compass (U), taxis (J), tropism (Z).

Detecting Changing States (page 232)

1. Any physical or chemical change in the environment, capable of provoking a response in an organism.

2. (a) and (b) any from the examples provided (or others). Answers provided as stimulus (receptor):
    (a) <u>External stimuli and their receptors</u>: Light (photoreceptor cells); gravity (hair cells/vestibule of the inner ear); sound/vibration (hair cells in

the cochlea of the inner ear); airborne chemicals (olfactory receptors in the nose); dissolved chemicals (taste buds); external pressure (dermal pressure receptors, e.g. Pacinian corpuscle, Meissner's corpuscles); pain (nerve endings in the dermis); temperature (nerve endings in the skin).

(b) <u>Internal stimuli and their receptors</u>: Blood pH/carbon dioxide level (chemoreceptors in blood vessels); blood pressure (baroreceptors); stretch (proprioreceptors, e.g. muscle spindle).

Nervous Regulation in Vertebrates (page 233)

1. (a) The **sensory receptors** receive sensory information (information about the environment) and respond by generating an electrical response (message).

(b) The **central nervous system** (CNS) processes the sensory input and coordinates an appropriate response (through motor output).

(c) A system of **effectors** bring about an appropriate response.
Note: Together these systems function to bring about appropriate (adaptive) responses to the environment so that homeostasis (steady state) is maintained.

2. Nervous control is rapid, it acts in the short term and its effects are short lived. In contrast, hormonal control is slower and it is longer acting.

Reflexes (page 234)

1. Conscious thought is not a preferable feature of reflexes because it **would slow down the response time**. The adaptive value of reflexes is in allowing a very rapid response to a stimulus, which would not be possible if higher reasoning was involved.

2. A spinal reflex involves integration within the spinal cord, e.g. knee jerk (monosynaptic) or pain withdrawal (polysynaptic). A cranial reflex involves integration within the brain stem (e.g. pupil reflex).

3. (a) A monosynaptic reflex arc involves just two neurons and one synapse (e.g. knee jerk reflex) and a polysynaptic reflex arc involves two synapses through a relay or interneuron, e.g. pain withdrawal.

(b) A monosynaptic reflex arc because there is one less synapse over which diffusion of neurotransmitter must occur.

4. (a) Newborn reflexes equip them with the appropriate survival behavior in their otherwise helpless state. One example such as; the rooting reflex helps them to locate a nipple, the suckling reflex insures feeding, the startle reflex induces crying, invoking a parental care response, the grasp reflex ensures they keep contact with the parent.

(b) The presence of these reflexes indicates appropriate development. An absence of reflex behaviors in newborns may indicate neural damage or developmental impairment.

Neuron Structure and Function (page 235)

1. Missing panels as follows:
<u>Length of fibers</u>:
Sensory neuron: Long dendrites, short axons
Motor neuron: Short dendrites, long axons

Function:
Sensory neuron: Conducts impulse to CNS
Motor neuron: Conducts impulse to effector (muscle or gland)

2. (a) Myelination increases the speed of impulse conduction.

(b) Oligodendrocytes

(c) Schwann cells

(d) Neurons in the PNS frequently have to transmit over long distances so speed of impulse conduction is critical to efficient function.

3. Myelin prevents ions from entering or leaving the axon along myelinated segments and so prevents leakage of charge across the neuron membrane. The current is carried in the cytoplasm so that the action potential at one node (gap in the sheath) is sufficient to trigger an action potential at the next. Myelin has another advantage too in reducing energy expenditure since fewer ions overall need to be pumped to restore resting potential after an action potential has passed.

4. (a) Faster conduction speeds enable more rapid responses to stimuli.

(b) Increasing axon diameter increases conduction velocity because it reduces the longitudinal resistance. This means that local currents can spread further.

5. The destruction of the myelin prevents those (previously myelinated) axons from conducting. Without insulation, the neuron membrane leaks ions and the local current is attenuated and insufficient to depolarize the next node. Also, myelinated axons only have gated channels at their nodes, so action potentials can only be generated at node regions in those axons that were previously myelinated.

Action Potentials (page 237)

1. (a) Neurons have the ability to conduct electrical impulses.

(b) Schwann cells cannot conduct electrical impulses.

2. An action potential passes along a nerve because the depolarization occurring in one region of the axon makes the next region of the axon more permeable to sodium ions (and more likely to conduct the impulse).

3. The nervous system interprets nerve impulses correctly because it records where they have come from and "knows" where they go to. Different regions of the brain are responsible for sorting out, interpreting, and integrating the nerve impulses from different sources.

5. NOTE: Attentive students will notice that this trace does not perfectly match the idealized schematic of an action potential (namely the hyperpolarization does not fall below threshold and resting potential is more positive than the starting resting potential). Differences in electrophysiological techniques used in recording lead to departures from the schematic. In this case, the real action potential is sitting atop a voltage offset caused by the current pulse used to stimulate the axon.

(a) B: Membrane depolarization
D: Hyperpolarization
E: Return to resting potential
C: Repolarization

A: The membrane's resting potential
(b) Point 1: Stimulus causes opening of Na^+ channels and Na^+ begins to flow into the cell.
(c) Rapid Na^+ influx = rapid depolarization.

Chemical Synapses (page 239)

1. A **synapse** is a junction between the end of one axon and the dendrite or cell body of a receiving neuron. **Note**: A synapse can also occur between the end of one axon and a muscle cell (neuromuscular junction).

2. Arrival of a nerve impulse at the end of the axon causes an influx of calcium. This induces the vesicles to release their neurotransmitter into the cleft.

3. Delay at the synapse is caused by the time it takes for the neurotransmitter to diffuse across the synaptic cleft.

4. (a) Neurotransmitter (NT) is degraded into component molecules by enzyme activity on the membrane of the receiving neuron (in this case, acetylcholin-esterase acts on Ach to produce acetyl and choline). This reference is to the cholinergic synapse pictured. Continued action of the NT at adrenergic synapses is prevented by reuptake of the NT (noradrenalin) by the presynaptic neuron.
   (b) The neurotransmitter must be deactivated so that it does not continue to stimulate the receiving neuron (continued stimulation would lead to depletion of neurotransmitter and fatigue of the nerve). Deactivation allows recovery of the neuron so that it can respond to further impulses.

5. Acetylcholine (either of):
   • It occurs at the synapse between motor neurons and muscle cells, where it causes depolarization of the muscle cell (and leads to muscle contraction).
   • Ach is released by all parasympathetic fibers (autonomic nervous system) where it may cause an excitatory or inhibitory response (depending on the postsynaptic receptor with which it interacts). **Note**: Ach is also released by preganglionic fibers in the sympathetic division of the ANS.

6. The amount of neurotransmitter released influences the response of the receiving cell (response strength is proportional to amount of neurotransmitter released).

Encoding Information (page 240)

1. Sensory receptors are termed '**biological transducers**' because they convert stimulus energy (e.g. electromagnetic radiation) into electrochemical energy (a change in membrane potential).

2. Linking the size of a sensory response to stimulus energy allows the incorporation (into the message) of valuable information about the strength of the stimulus (i.e. is the stimulus worth responding to or not).

3. Sensory adaptation allows the nervous system to cease responding to constant stimuli that do not change in intensity. This prevents nervous system overstimulation and allows constant, background sensory information to be ignored.

4. It is important that a receptor does not respond to stimuli at sub-threshold intensities as this could mean the receptor would be responding inappropriately

and too often. **Note**: The threshold level is a stimulus intensity that is established through natural selection as appropriate in the prevailing environment and (like other biological responses) is subject to change over time.

Integration at Synapses (page 241)

1. Integration refers to the interpretation and coordination (by the central nervous system) of inputs from many sources (inputs may be inhibitory or excitatory).

2. (a) **Summation**: The additive effect of presynaptic inputs (impulses) in the postsynaptic cell (neuron or muscle fiber).
   (b) **Spatial summation** refers to the summation of impulses from **separate** axon terminals arriving simultaneously at the postsynaptic cell. **Temporal summation** refers to the arrival of several impulses from a **single** axon terminal in rapid succession (postsynaptic responses are so close together in time that they can sum to generate an AP).

3. (a) **Acetylcholine** is the NT involved; arrival of an action potential (AP) at the neuromuscular junction causes the release of Ach from the synaptic knobs.
   (b) Ach causes **depolarization** of the postsynaptic membrane (in this case, the sarcolemma). The depolarization in response to the arrival of an AP at the postsynaptic cell is essentially the same as that occurring at any excitatory synapse involving Ach.

Drugs at Synapses (page 242)

1. (a) and (b) any of in any order:
   • Drug can act as a direct agonist, binding to and activating Ach receptors on the postsynaptic membrane, e.g. nicotine.
   • Drug can act as an indirect agonist, preventing the breakdown of Ach, thereby causing continued response in the postsynaptic cell, e.g. therapeutic drugs used to treat Alzheimer's disease.
   • Drug can act as an antagonist, competing for Ach binding sites and reducing or blocking the response of the postsynaptic cell, e.g. atropine or curare.

2. Atropine and curare are direct antagonists because they compete for the same binding sites (as Ach) on the postsynaptic membrane (hence **direct**) and they block sodium influx so that impulses are not generated (hence **antagonist** = against the usual action).

3. Curare is used to cause flaccid paralysis (relaxed or without tone) to the isolated abdominal region in order to facilitate operative procedure (of course, the drug is administered as a carefully produced formulation).

The Vertebrate Brain (page 243)

1. (a) In mammals there has been a huge expansion in the cerebral region of the brain. In mammals, visual processing is a function of the forebrain (there is no distinct optic lobe).
   (b) The size of a sensory processing region in the brain reflects the importance of that sense to the animal.

2. The more primitive parts of the brain associated with autonomic functions (e.g. medulla oblongata) have remained largely unchanged during the course of vertebrate evolution. Other parts of the brain associated

with sensory perception, coordination, and higher brain functions, such as learning and (in humans) reasoning, have changed considerably. These changes reflect either the importance of particular senses to the animal (e.g. larger regions for processing visual or olfactory information), or they reflect the fact that different parts of the brain take over the processing of certain kinds of information (e.g. in mammals, the analysis of vision is a higher brain (forebrain) function). Increasing complexity in the forebrain is associated with more complex (particularly, social) behaviors, and increasing reliance on learning and behavioral flexibility. Also associated with this, and with increased complexity of movement generally, the cerebellum has also increased in size.

The Human Brain (page 244)
1. (a) Breathing/heartbeat: brainstem (medulla)
   (b) Memory/emotion: cerebrum
   (c) Posture/balance: cerebellum
   (d) Autonomic functions: hypothalamus
   (e) Visual processing: occipital lobe
   (f) Body temperature: hypothalamus
   (g) Language: motor and sensory speech areas
   (h) Muscular contraction: primary motor area
   (i) Sensory processing related to taste: primary gustatory area
   (j) Sensory processing related to sound: auditory areas

2. The brain is protected against physical damage and infection by the bony skull, by the meninges overlying the delicate brain tissue, and by the fluid-filled ventricles, which absorb shocks and deliver nutritive substances (via cerebrospinal fluid) to the brain tissue. The blood-brain barrier formed by the endothelial tight junctions of capillaries surrounding the brain is also the main protection against toxins and infection as microbes and many large molecules cannot cross it.

3. (a) The CSF is produced by the choroid plexuses, which are the capillary clusters on the roof of each ventricle. It circulates through the ventricles and returns to the blood via projections of the arachnoid membrane.
   (b) If this return flow is blocked, fluid builds up in the ventricles causing hydrocephalus, and consequently pressure on the brain tissue and brain damage.

Imaging the Brain (page 246)
1. (a) X-ray images of the body are taken from multiple angles and in multiple slices. Computer software generates a 3-D image of the body. CT scans work best on dense material such as bone, but iodine-based contrast agents can be used to enhance some tissue (e.g. blood vessels).
   (b) The patient is exposed to high energy x-rays (radiation) which may increase the risk of the patient developing cancer. The scan time is limited to about one second to minimise risk. **Note:** Some patients also have allergic reactions to the iodine substances used to improve the resolution of the image.

2. (a) MRI scans give better images of soft tissue than CT scans can. The patient is not exposed to any radiation during MRI scans.
   (b) fMRI maps the change in blood flow related to neural activity in the brain. fMRI can be used to identify which regions of the brain are affected

in Alzheimer's patients. fMRI could be used to examine the effectiveness of future Alzheimer's treatments on brain activity.
(c) Patients with metal body parts can not be scanned because of the magnetic field.

The Malfunctioning Brain: Alzheimer's (page 247)
1. Alzheimer's results when neurons, and their connections, are lost at an accelerated rate in the brain. Loss of processing ability affects a number of functions including memory, reasoning and language.

2. A mutation for the APP gene has been discovered within families who demonstrate a history of Alzheimer's. The protein is thought to be involved in synapse formation and neural plasticity.

3. Alzheimer's sufferers suffer an accelerated loss of neurons and show reduced brain activity, particularly in regions that are important for memory and intellectual processing, such as the cerebral cortex and hippocampus.
   Teacher's note: The most recent evidence indicates that, during normal aging, there is a loss of synaptic function in the brain, but the neurons themselves are not lost. In Alzheimer's, there is a pathological loss of the neurons themselves.

Dopamine and Behavior (page 248)
1. Behavior is based on both genetics and the environment. Although genes may predispose a person to behaving in a certain way, the environment plays a major part in whether or not that behavior is carried out. In addition, interactions between genes influence their final expression in the phenotype, so it becomes difficult to identify which gene is the 'cause' of the behavior. Diet also has a major effect on behavior (through physiological mechanisms) with many studies showing that artificial colorings and flavourings can affect behavior in young people. Finally, human thought must be included. Humans can consciously alter their behavior in response to peer pressures and societal expectations (although again, both the environment and genetics play a part in this process).

2. Required answers in bold. Different dopamine levels are directly associated with certain behaviors. **Low levels may cause people to become highly active**. Dopamine levels increase when active and give the body a sense of wellbeing and satisfaction. In order to achieve this feeling, people with naturally low levels are often more active than normal as the body tries to produce more dopamine. **Low levels are also associated with tendencies towards addiction**, as the feelings gained from certain drugs are interpreted by the body as similar to dopamine and there is a physiological craving to maintain the feeling. **High levels of dopamine are associated with** fixation on certain objects and **increased sensory perception** in a way that may cause people to hear and see things in an exaggerated way. **Extremely high levels are associated with schizophrenia** (a split between what is real and what is not) where the body begins to hear and see things that are not there.

3. Natural variations in the DRD4 gene affect its ability to produce receptors that bind with dopamine. Protein chains that are too long do not fold correctly and produce receptors that do not efficiently bind to dopamine. In this case the body will perceive the levels of dopamine to be low and act in a way to increase them (frequently by increasing activity).

4. Dopamine is present in a number of neural pathways. The link between the DRD4 gene and dopamine levels allows us to theorize that other neural pathways are affected by similar receptor genes. The link between a behavior and a gene sets a precedence for finding other genes that affect behavior. It lends weight to the theory that human behavior is more influenced by genetics than by the environment.

Chemical Imbalances in the Brain (page 249)

1. Neurotransmitters are chemicals that transfer signals between neurons across a synapse (synaptic cleft). A neurotransmitter is released from the presynaptic neuron into the synaptic cleft where it interacts with a postsynaptic neuron to cause a response. The amount of neurotransmitter released influences the response of the receiving cell.

2. (a) Parkinson's disease is caused by a reduction in dopamine production due to the loss of nerve cells in the substantia nigra region of the brain. This reduces the stimulation in the motor cortex and results in slow physical movement and uncontrollable tremors.
   (b) Depression is caused by reduced serotonin released from the raphe nuclei resulting in reduced stimulation of neurons in the brain, but especially those related to emotion. People with depression often have feelings of low self esteem, guilt, regret, and suffer physical tiredness.

3. L-dopa is a precursor to dopamine, it can cross the blood-brain barrier where it is converted to dopamine. Dopamine stimulates the motor cortex, reducing the physical effects of Parkinson's. Dopamine can not be used as a treatment because it can not cross the blood-brain barrier, it therefore has no direct effect.

4. Antidepressants work by increasing serotonin levels in the brain. They have two main modes of action. SSRIs stop serotonin reabsorption by the presynaptic neuron (this causes increased serotonin levels and greater stimulation of the postsynaptic neurone). MAOIs prevent the breakdown of serotonin in the synaptic cleft once it has been released from the presynaptic neuron.

5. Ecstasy and SSRIs both increase relative serotonin levels. SSRIs prevent the presynaptic neurons reabsorbing serotonin from the synaptic cleft. Ecstasy works in two ways. It prevents serotonin re-uptake from the synaptic cleft, and also causes the serotonin transporters to work in reverse, flooding serotonin into the synaptic cleft and increasing its levels.

6. The huge spikes in serotonin secretion eventually lead to depletion of levels in the brain because the serotonin production cannot keep pace with the increased secretion. This results in depression, psychiatric disorders, and memory problems.

The Structure of the Eye (page 251)

1. (a) Cornea: Responsible for most of the refraction (bending) of the incoming light.
   (b) Ciliary body: Secretes the aqueous humour which helps to maintain the shape of the eye and assists in refraction.
   (c) Iris: Regulates the amount of light entering the eye for vision in bright and dim light.

2. (a) The incoming light is refracted (primarily by the cornea, but also by the lens and fluid filled cavities of the eye) and the amount entering the eye is regulated by constriction of the pupil. The degree of refraction is adjusted through accommodation (changes to the shape of the lens) so that a sharp image is formed on the retina.
   (b) Accommodation is achieved by the action of the ciliary muscles pulling on the elastic lens and changing its shape.
   When the ciliary muscle contracts there is decreased pressure on the suspensory ligament and the lens becomes more convex (to focus on near objects). When the ciliary muscle relaxes there is increased tension on the suspensory ligament and the lens is pulled into a thinner shape (to focus on distant objects).

3. (a) The pupil is the hole through which light enters the eye. By constricting (in bright light), the pupil can narrow the diameter of this entry point and prevent light rays entering from the periphery. In dim light, the opposite happens; the pupil expands to allow more light into the eye.
   (b) Control of over the entry of light is appropriate as a reflex activity because the response is immediate and unconscious. In this way, the eye can be protected against damage and vision optimized without the need to consider the action necessary (which would be slow and inefficient).

4. (a) Image (point of focus) is in front of the retina.
   (b) Image (point of focus) is behind the retina.

5. (a) Myopia: Concave lens diverges the incoming light rays so that they have to travel further through the eyeball and are focused directly on the retina.
   (b) Hypermetropia: Convex lens converges incoming light so that the image falls directly on the retina.

The Physiology of Vision (page 253)

1. (a) The retina is the layer of light sensitive tissue lining the inner surface of the eye. It comprises several layers of neurons, including the photoreceptor rods and cones, interconnected by synapses. Light induces the production of neural signals in the rods and cones, which are processed by other neurons of the retina.
   (b) The optic nerve is formed from the axons of the retinal ganglion cells, which carry the processed neural signals, the form of action potentials, from the retina through the optic chiasma to the visual cortex in the cerebrum. It also contains the blood vessels supplying the retina.

2. The **blind spot** is where all the nerve fibers leave the eye as the optic nerve to reach the brain. There are no photoreceptor cells there (hence "blind"). In contrast, the **fovea** has the greatest density of photoreceptor cells and hence it is the point of most acute vision.

ISBN 978-1-927173-14-5 | © **BIOZONE** International 2012

3.

Feature	Rod cells	Cone cells
Visual pigment(s):	Rhodopsin (no color vision)	Iodopsin (three types)
Visual acuity:	Low	High
Overall function:	Vision in dim light, high sensitivity	Color vision, vision in bright light

4. Many **rod** cells synapse with each bipolar cell and this gives poor acuity but high sensitivity. Each **cone** cell synapses with only one bipolar cell and this gives high acuity but poor sensitivity.

5. Hubel and Wiesel's experiments showed that if visual stimuli were impaired during certain developmental periods in young kittens, their vision did not develop normally. This is because specific neural connections were not made, and the development of the neural pathways did not proceed normally.

Hearing (page 255)

1. (a) **Ear drum** vibrates in response to sound waves.
   (b) **Ear ossicles** transmit the sound waves from the ear drum to the smaller oval window.
   (c) **Oval window** amplifies the sound waves before they enter the fluid filled inner ear (because of its smaller surface area).
   (d) **Sensory hair cells** respond to the stimulus of pressure waves in the fluid filled inner ear by generating electrical impulses.
   (e) **Auditory nerve** transmits the impulses from the sensory hair cells to the brain for processing.

2. Sound waves are converted into pressure waves in the fluid. Because fluid is non-compressible, the pressure wave moves the membranes in the cochlea, causing the hair cells to be stimulated.

Taste and Smell (page 256)

1. Chemical sense relies on the chemicals (scent molecules) binding to membrane-bound sensory receptors and inducing a change in membrane potential in the sensory cell (signal transduction). These electrochemical messages are relayed to the appropriate centers in the brain where they are interpreted.

2. Example only:
   10 s: 1 (very strong)
   20 s: 2 (quite strong)
   30 s: 3 (noticeable)
   40 s: 4 (weak)
   50 s: 5 (very faint)
   60 s: 6 (could not detect)

3. (a) The sense of smell (to that scent) declines.
   (b) Sensory adaptation. The sensory cells adapt to the stimulus and cease responding to it.
   (c) It is adaptive to stop responding to stimuli that are constantly present and do not change in intensity. Appropriate responses are directed to new stimuli.

The Mechanics of Movement (page 257)

1. (a) Prime mover: the muscle primarily responsible for the movement.
   (b) Antagonist: the muscle that opposes the prime mover. i.e. relaxes when prime mover contracts.

Its action can be protective in preventing over-stretching of the prime mover during contraction.
   (c) Synergist: assists the prime mover by fine-tuning the direction of limb movement.

2. Muscles can only contract and relax, therefore they can only pull on a bone; they cannot push it. To produce movement, two muscles must act as **antagonistic** pairs to move a bone to and from different positions.

3. Muscles have an origin on one (less moveable) bone and an insertion on another (more moveable) bone. When the muscle contracts across the joint connecting the two bones, the insertion moves towards the origin, therefore moving the limb. To raise a limb, the flexor (prime mover in this case) contracts pulling the limb bone up (extensor/antagonist relaxed). To lower the limb, the extensor contracts, pulling the limb down (flexor relaxed).

4. Bones are rigid and movement occurs only at joints. The degree of movement allowed depends the type of joint. The bones of the limbs, which need to be freely moveable are connected by synovial joints. Body parts where movement is not desirable, such as the joints of the skull, are largely rigid.

5. (a) Radius (radial tuberosity)
   (b) Ulna
   (c) Triceps
   (d) Rotation of ulna and radius

6. (a) Elbow extension
   (b) Triceps

7. (a) Nodding head = flexion and extension
   (b) Hitching a ride = abduction

Muscle Structure and Function (page 259)

1. Smooth muscle, also called involuntary muscle, has spindle shaped cells with one central nucleus per cell and a smooth appearance with no striations. Its contractions are diffuse and it is not under conscious control so it is involved in movement of visceral organs such as the gut. Striated (skeletal) muscle is voluntary and is responsible for the skeletal muscle movement over which we have conscious control. It has a striated or striped appearance and the cells are multinucleate with peripheral nuclei. Cardiac muscle is involuntary muscle responsible for the contraction of the heart. Although it is striated, it does not fatigue in the same way as skeletal muscle. There is one nucleus per cell and structures called intercalated discs (electrical junctions) join individual cells.

2. (a) The banding pattern results from the overlap pattern of the thick and thin filaments (dark = thick and thin filaments overlapping, light = no overlap).
   (b) I band: Becomes narrower as more filaments overlap and the area of non-overlap decreases.
   H zone: Disappears as the overlap becomes maximal (no region of only thick filaments).
   Sarcomere: Shortens progressively as the overlap becomes maximal.

3. They protect the muscle from friction and give structural integrity to the tissue. The perimysium (surrounding the fascicles) may also be involved in transmitting contractile movements across the muscle.

4. The all-or-none response refers to the way in which an individual muscle fiber contracts maximally (if the stimulus is strong enough) or not at all (if it is not).

5. Without dystrophin there is no structural link between the muscle fibers and the extracellular matrix. Calcium penetrates the plasma membrane (sarcolemma) of the muscle cells and damages them, eventually destroying the muscle cells (fibers).

The Sliding Filament Theory (page 261)

1. (a) Myosin: Has a moveable head that provides a power stroke when activated.
   (b) Actin: Two protein molecules twisted in a double helix that form the thin filament of a myofibril.
   (c) Calcium ions: Bind to the blocking molecules, causing them to move and expose the myosin binding site.
   (d) Troponin-tropomyosin: Bind to actin molecule in a way that prevents myosin head from forming a cross bridge.
   (e) ATP: Supplies energy for flexing of the myosin head (power stroke).

2. (a) By changing the frequency of stimulation, so that fibers receive impulses at a greater rate (frequency summation).
   (b) By changing the number and size of motor units recruited (a few motor units = a small contraction, maximum number of motor units = maximum contraction).

3. (a) Calcium ions and ATP.
   (b) Calcium ions are released from a store in the sarcoplasmic reticulum when an action potential arrives. ATP is present in the muscle fiber and is hydrolyzed by ATPase enzymes on the myosin.

Muscle Tone and Posture (page 262)

1. (a) Muscle tone is the continuous and passive partial contraction of muscles giving a firm appearance.
   (b) At any one time, a few fibers in a muscle are always contracting involuntarily (different fibers at different times).

2. (a) The **muscle spindle organ** monitors the degree of stretch (contraction) in a muscle and provides information to bring about adjustment of contraction.
   (b) **Intrafusal fibers parallel to extrafusal fibers**: When the muscle relaxes, it lengthens and the muscle spindle is stretched. The stretching results in a reflex adjustment of contraction (usually to maintain tone).
   Sensory neurons in non-contractile region: When non-contractile portion is stretched (it cannot, itself, adjust its length), sensory neurons are stimulated.
   Motor neuron synapses: When the motor impulses arrive to adjust state of contraction, both the extrafusal and intrafusal fibers are adjusted appropriately.

KEY TERMS: Crossword (page 263)

Answers Across
2. Action potential
4. Effectors

Answers Down
1. Neuron
3. Neuromuscular junction

8. Neurotransmitters
9. Brain
10. Cardiac muscle
11. Cholinergic
13. Brain stem
17. Resting potential
19. Biological transducer
20. Olfaction
21. Eyes
23. Skeletal muscle
24. Threshold potential
26. Depolarization

5. Central nervous system
6. Sarcomere
7. Receptor
12. Retina
14. Cerebrum
15. Smooth muscle
16. Dopamine
18. Cerebellum
22. Synapse
25. Rod

Biomes (page 266)

1. (a) Tundra: D
   (b) Temperate deciduous forest: H
   (c) Deserts: C
   (d) Dry tropical forest: B
   (e) Evergreen conifer forest: F
   (f) Prairie grasslands: A
   (g) Savannah grasslands: E
   (h) Tropical rain forest: G

2. Low rainfall, high temperatures (leading to drying out) in lower latitudes. Low sunshine hours, low temperatures in higher latitudes.

Components of an Ecosystem (page 267)

1. A **community** is a naturally occurring group of organisms living together as an ecological entity. The community is the biological part of the ecosystem. The **ecosystem** includes all of the organisms (the community) and their physical environment.

2. The **biotic factors** are the influences that result from the activities of living organisms in the community whereas the **abiotic** (physical) **factors** comprise the non-living part of the community, e.g. climate.

3. (a) Population   (c) The community
   (b) Ecosystem   (d) Physical factor

Habitat (page 268)

1. An organism will occupy habitat according to its range of tolerance for a particular suite of conditions (temperature, vegetation and cover, pH, conductivity). Organisms will tend to occupy those regions where all or most of their requirements are met and will avoid those regions where they are not. Sometimes, a single factor, e.g. pH for an aquatic organisms, will limit occupation of an otherwise suitable habitat.

2. (a) Most of a species population is found in the optimum range because this is the zone where conditions for that species are best; most of the population will select that zone.
   (b) The greatest constraint on an organism growth within its optimum range would be competition between it and members of the same species (or perhaps different species with similar niche requirements).

3. In a marginal niche, any of the following might apply:
   – Physicochemical conditions (e.g. temperature, current speed, pH, conductivity) might be sub-optimal and create stress (therefore greater

vulnerability to disease).
- Food might be more scarce or of lower quality/ nutritional value.
- Mates might be harder to find.
- The area might be more exposed to predators.
- Resting, sleeping, or nesting places might be harder to find and/or less suitable in terms of shelter or safety.
- Competition from other better-adapted species might be more intense.

Sampling Communities (page 269)

1. We sample populations in order to gain information about their abundance and composition. Sampling is necessary because, in most cases, populations are too large to examine in total.

2. (a) Random or systematic quadrat sampling.
   (b) Random or systematic point sampling (using a net or trap).
   (c) Line transect with point sampling (from low to high altitude). If time for sampling and analysis is not constrained, a belt transect using quadrats at regular intervals would provide the most information.

3. Information about the physical environment helps to explain species distributions. Certain species are usually associated with a particular suite of physical factors (e.g. preferred exposure, temperature, humidity etc) and if these are measured and known, more information on community patterns can be gathered.

4. As the vertical distance up the trunk increases, light intensity and temperature increase and humidity declines. With these changes in physical conditions there is consequent change in the vegetation from a diverse community of shade and moisture adapted moss species, to a community comprising just one species of (hardier) tree moss and various species of lichens, i.e. species more tolerant of the microclimate of lower humidity and higher light and temperature.

Quadrat Sampling (page 271)

1. Mean number of centipedes captured per quadrat: Total number centipedes ÷ total number quadrats
   = 30 individuals ÷ 37 quadrats
   = 0.811 centipedes per quadrat

2. Number per quadrat ÷ area of each quadrat
   $0.811 ÷ 0.08 = 10.1$ centipedes per m^2

3. Clumped or random distribution.

4. Presence of suitable microhabitats for cover (e.g. logs, stones, leaf litter) may be scattered.

Quadrat-Based Estimates (page 272)

1. Species abundance in plant communities can be determined by using quadrats and transects, and abundance scales are often appropriate. Methods for sampling animal communities are more diverse, and density is a more common measure of abundance.

2. Quadrat must be large enough to be representative and small enough to minimize sampling effort.

3. **Habitat heterogeneity** - diverse habitats require more samples to be representative because they are not homogeneous.

4. (a) and (b) any two of:
   - The values assigned to species on the abundance scale are subjective and may not be consistent between users.
   - An abundance scale may miss rarer species and overestimate conspicuous ones.
   - The scale may be inappropriate for use in some habitats.
   - The semi-quantitative values assigned to the abundance categories cover a range so results will lack precision.

The Ecological Niche (page 273)

1. (a) The realized niche constitutes only a small proportion of the niche range which an organism can occupy. It is mainly determined by interspecific competition, so can expand or contract depending on the level of competition at the time.
   (b) Two or more of: Direct or indirect competition with other species for resources such as food, resting or breeding sites, nesting material or other resources. Predation pressure. Presence of parasites.

2. Organisms have different niche requirements in terms of their tolerance to abiotic factors and the other species with which they interact. Environmental gradients in ecosystems provide opportunity for particular species assemblages to occur at specific zones. Species will occupy the zones to which they are best suited. Competition and poor tolerance of abiotic factors outside this restrict them to this zone.

Adaptation and Niche (page 274)

For each of the following the list is not exhaustive, but uses examples given on the diagrams. Note that most adaptations have components of structure, physiology, and behavior (e.g. threat behaviors involve use of structural features. Thermoregulatory physiology involves some behavior etc.). Categories may not be mutually exclusive.

1. Common mole adaptations:
   (a) **Structural**: Generally these are adaptations to aid efficient digging and tunneling, assisting survival though protection and effective food gathering. Clawed hindfeet push soil out of the way when digging (improves efficiency). External ear openings are covered by fur to protect them when digging. Short, powerful limbs with efficient lever arrangement of muscles and joints aids rotation-thrust movement in digging. Forefeet powerfully clawed as digging tools. Velvety fur reduces friction when moving through the soil. Fur can lie in either direction so backward movement in tunnel is not hampered. Tubular body shape aids movement underground. Heavily buttressed head and neck makes tunneling easier and more energy efficient.
   (b) **Physiological**: Well developed chemical sense aids location of food. Good sense of hearing.
   (c) **Behavioral**: Solitary and territorial behavior (except when breeding) helps to maintain a viable food supply and reduce aggressive encounters. Sleep and feed underground offering effective protection from predators.

2. Snow bunting adaptations:

(a) **Structural**: large amount of white plumage reduces heat loss, white feathers are hollow and air filled (acting as good insulators).

(b) **Physiological**: Lay one or two more eggs than (ecologically) equivalent species further south producing larger broods (improving breeding success), rapid molt to winter plumage is suited to the rapid seasonal changes of the Arctic.

(c) **Behavioral**: feeding activity continues almost uninterrupted during prolonged daylight hours (allowing large broods to be raised and improving survival and breeding success), migration to overwintering regions during Arctic winter (escapes harsh Arctic winter), will burrow into snow drifts for shelter (withstand short periods of very bad weather), males assist in brood rearing (improved breeding success).

3. (a) The leaf has been modified by rolling, with the sides fused into a keel, so that it forms a hollow organ to trap and digest insects. The leaf has a brightly colored lip to attract insects, and gland cells in the leaf base to produce digestive enzymes.

(b) Leaves are modified into paired, lobed structures fringed with trigger hairs along one edge. Along the 'hinge' region of each leaf, specialized cells enable rapid closure of the trap to capture insects.

4. Because of the high energy cost of being carnivorous (leaf modification, production of digestive enzymes), carnivorous plants are less able to compete with other plants in conditions where nitrogen is not limiting.

Physical Factors and Gradients (page 276)

1. Whereas **climate** refers to longer term, usually broad scale weather patterns in a region, the **microclimate** refers to climatic variation in a very small area or in a particular habitat. This can vary depending on shelter and aspect, as well as the influence of objects in the environment. It often refers to the immediate climate in which an organism lives.

2. High humidity underground, in cracks, under rocks.

3. In a crack or crevice, in a burrow underground, in spaces under rocks.

4. An animal unable to find suitable shelter would undergo heat stress, dehydration and eventually die.

5. High humidity enables land animals to reduce their water loss due to evaporation. This in turn reduces their demand for (and dependence on) drinkable water.

6. At night, temperature drops and humidity increases (to the point where condensation may occur; this is a source of valuable water for some invertebrates).

Physical Factors in a Forest (page 277)

1. Environmental gradients from canopy to leaf litter:
   (a) Light intensity: decreases.
   (b) Wind speed: decreases.
   (c) Humidity: increases.

2. Reasons why factors change:
   (a) Light intensity: Foliage above will shade plants below, with a cumulative effect. The forest floor receives light that has been reflected off leaf surfaces several times, or passed through leaves.

   (b) Wind speed: Canopy trees act as a wind-break, reducing wind velocity. Subcanopy trees will reduce the velocity even further, until near the ground the wind may be almost non-existent. An opening in the forest canopy (a clearing) can expose the interior of the forest to higher wind velocities.

   (c) Humidity: The sources of humidity (water vapor) are the soil moisture, leaf litter, and the transpiration from plants. Near the canopy, the wind will carry away moisture-laden air. Near the forest floor, there is little wind, and humidity levels are high.

3. The color of the light will change nearer the forest floor. White light (all wavelengths) falling on the canopy will be absorbed by the leaves. Reflected light in the green wavelength bounces off the leaves and passes downward to lower foliage and the forest floor.

Stratification in a Forest (page 278)

1. Stratified forests have distinctive layers each with its own microclimate. As a result, the diversity of habitats is much greater than found in a forest with less vertical structure. For example, trees in the canopy layer receive full sun, but must be adapted to cope with higher winds. Plants in the ground layer must be shade adapted as very little sunlight filters down to the ground, but they do not need to be adapted to cope with wind.

2. Removal of emergents and large canopy trees opens up gaps in the canopy, altering the physical factors within the forest. More sunlight reaches lower levels of the forest, trees previously under the canopy trees may receive more precipitation, and trees in the subcanopy may be exposed to more wind. Removal of canopy trees may give other species an opportunity to flourish, as a result the composition of the forest may change.

Transect Sampling (page 279)

1. (a) With transects of any length (10 m or more), sampling (and sample analysis) using this method is very time consuming and labor intensive.

   (b) Line transects, although quicker than belt transects, may not be representative of the community. There may be many species which are present but which do not touch the line and are not recorded.

   (c) Belt transects use a wider strip along the study area and there is much less chance that a species will not be recorded.

   (d) It is not appropriate to use transects in situations involving highly mobile organisms.

2. To test whether or not the transect sampling interval was sufficient to accurately sample the community, the sampling interval could be decreased (e.g. from a sampling interval of every 1.5 m to an interval of every 0.25 m). If no more species are detected and the trends along the transect remain the same, then the sampling interval was adequate.

3. Distribution of *Littorina* species along a rocky shore (figure is laterally compressed to fit the A5 format).

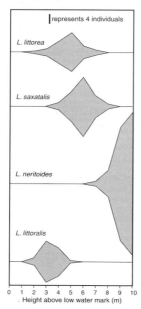

represents 4 individuals

L. littorea

L. saxatalis

L. neritoides

L. littoralis

0 1 2 3 4 5 6 7 8 9 10
Height above low water mark (m)

Community Change with Altitude (page 281)

1. Altitude change: 2228 − 790 = 1438 m

2. Temperature, precipitation (snow, rain), soil type.

3. **Berridale**:

Altitude: 790 m   Precipitation: 500 mm
Temperature: 12°C   Soil: Light, textured

Wilson's Valley:

Altitude: 1370 m   Precipitation: 1100 mm
Temperature: 6.5°C   Soil: Transitional humus

Mt. Kosciusko:

Altitude: 2228 m   Precipitation: 3300 mm
Temperature: 2°C   Soil: Alpine humus

4. Decreases (in a more or less linear fashion).

5. Increases (more or less exponentially).

6. The lower soil temperature inhibits the growth and metabolism of the decomposer organisms.

7. Zonation (or altitudinal zonation).

8. (a) Altitude range: 1150-1400 m
   (b) Insufficient rainfall
   (c) Temperature too low (too cold)

9. Any one of: Air pressure, partial pressure of oxygen and carbon dioxide, generally increased wind exposure.

10. Any one of: Tidal range over a coastal ecosystem, e.g. rocky shore, sandy beach, or mudflat. Deeper water ecosystems, e.g. lakes or coastal ecosystem below the tidal range.

Physical Factors on a Rocky Shore (page 283)

1. Environmental gradients:
   (a) Salinity: Increases from LWM to HWM
   (b) Temperature: Increases from LWM to HWM
   (c) Dissolved oxygen: Decreases from LWM to HWM
   (d) Exposure: Increases from LWM to HWM

2. Rock pools may have very high salinity due to evaporation after long exposure times without rain.

3. (a) **Mechanical force of wave action**: Point B will receive the full force of waves moving inshore, Point A will receive only milder backwash, Point C will experience some surge but no direct wave impacts. **Surface temperature**: Points A and B will experience greater variations in rock temperature depending on whether the tide is in or out, day or night, water temperature, wind chill. Point C is more protected from some of these factors and will not experience the warming effect of direct sunlight.
   (b) Microclimate.

Shoreline Zonation (page 284)

1. (a) Exposure time determines the species that can extend higher up the shore where the exposure time is longer. Some species will not tolerate long exposure times, others are very tolerant.
   (b) Two of: Intensity of wave action, salinity, temperature, or oxygen level (in pools).
   (c) Presence or absence of competing species, presence or absence of predators.

2. Broad bands approximately parallel to the water's edge, formed by distinct assemblages of species.

Seaweed Zonation (page 285)

1. (a) Percentage cover of each seaweed species.
   (b) Seaweed vigor and degree of dessication.

2. Column graph:

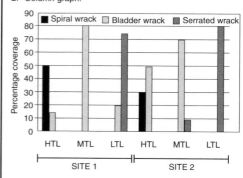

3. Spiral wrack is the most tolerant of exposure, and it grows vigorously in exposed regions despite showing evidence of desiccation. Bladder wrack grows throughout the midlittoral and is relatively tolerant of exposure, only showing signs of desiccation higher on the shore where exposure times are longer. Serrated wrack is intolerant of exposure and grows vigorously at the LTL but shows signs of desiccation above this and cannot compete with the more tolerant bladder wrack.

4. Quadrat position was staggered for the two sites to give a better indication of the extent of each species' distribution. The disadvantage is that the sites cannot be directly compared.

Sampling a Rocky Shore community
(page 286)

The results *per se* are not particularly important, but it is important to understand the method and its limitations. The results will vary depending on a group's agreed criteria for inclusion of organisms in a given quadrat (e.g. when and how an organism is counted when it is partly inside a quadrat). **Note**: Some algae are almost obscured by organisms or have other algae on top of them.

6. Typical results (total for each category) are:

	A	B	C	D	Direct count
Barnacle:	9	6	6	16	80
Oyster borer:	0	0	1	1	3
Chiton:	1	0	1	0	3
Limpet:	0	3	0	0	6
Algae:	27	18	15	13	101

7. Typical results for calculated population density based on A-D and on a direct count (question 8b):

	A	B	C	D	Direct count
Barnacle:	1667	1111	1111	2963	2469
Oyster borer:	0	0	185	185	93
Chiton:	185	0	185	0	93
Limpet:	0	556	0	0	185
Algae:	5000	3333	2778	2407	3117

NB: Area of 6 quadrats = $(0.03 \times 0.03) \times 6 = 0.0054 \, m^2$
Area of total sample area = $0.18 \times 0.18 = 0.0324 \, m^2$

8. (a) Once the quadrats have been laid, the animals moving from one quadrat to another could be counted twice. The quadrat could involve the placement of physical barriers between each quadrat (what about the invertebrates directly underneath?). Possibility of exposing the entire area and photographing it for later analysis.

(b) Densities calculated on direct count in the last column of the table above. Students should be aware of the dangers of extrapolating data from a small sample. Including or excluding single individuals can have a large effect on the density calculated, particularly where species are present at low densities. **Extension**: Groups could combine data to see if they get a more representative sample (i.e. closer to the direct count).

Interspecific Competition and Zonation
(page 288)

1. (a) A represents the **realized niche** of *Chthamalus*.
(b) When *Balanus* is removed from the lower shore, the range of *Chthalamus* extends into areas previously occupied by the *Balanus*. *Balanus* normally excludes *Chthamalus* from the lower shore.

2. Species will be distributed according to their various tolerances to abiotic factors and the interactions they have with other species in the community. Species are generally more restricted in their distribution than would

be predicted by their tolerances to physical factors. Competition, predation and other species interactions will constrain distribution and may determine species presence or absence in a particular area. For example, both the plicate and columnar barnacles occupy intertidal regions with some wave exposure. The columnar barnacle is more tolerant of exposure than the plicate barnacle and extends higher up the shore, where the time out of water is greater. Where the zones of the two species overlap, they compete for space and resources and both species are less abundant than they would be in the absence of competition

Field Study of a Rocky Shore (page 289)

1. Hypothesis (c): The communities of intertidal animals differ between exposed rocky shores and sheltered rocky shores.

2. Table see next page

3. Graph see next page.

4. (a) Brown and plicate barnacles have a preference for exposed rocky shores.
(b) Oyster borers are predators of brown and plicate barnacles so are more abundant when brown and plicate barnacles are also abundant.

5. Rock oyster

6. Discussion should not just revisit results without an explanation as to probable causal factors.

"We investigated the difference in rock based communities between an exposed rocky shore (sample site A), which experienced heavy waves and heavy waves, and a sheltered rock shore (sample site B), which experienced little wave action and low winds. Brown and plicate barnacles were found to be the most common on the exposed rocky shore, suggesting that is their preferred habitat. Oyster borer numbers were also higher on exposed rocky shores. This can perhaps be explained by the fact that they prey upon brown and plicate barnacles. Their lower numbers on sheltered rocky shores can be related to the fact the brown and plicate barnacle numbers are also lower on sheltered rocky shores. It was also found that rock oyster numbers were more prevalent on sheltered rocky shores. This may be due to the fact that they find it difficult to settle on rocks in heavy waves."

Physical Factors in a Small Lake (page 292)

1. Environmental gradients from water surface to bottom:
(a) Water temperature: Decreases gradually until below the zone of mixing when there is a sharp drop.
(b) Dissolved O_2: Oxygen at a uniform concentration until below the zone of mixing when there is a sharp drop, with very little oxygen at the bottom.
(c) Light penetration: Decreases at an exponential rate (most light is absorbed near the surface).

2. (a) Prevents mixing of the oxygen-rich surface water with the deeper oxygen-deficient water (represents a thermal barrier).
(b) Organisms (particularly bacteria) living below the thermocline use up much of the available oxygen. Decomposition also uses up oxygen.

Table: Total and mean numbers of intertidal animals at two rocky shore sites.

		Brown barnacle	Oyster borer	Columnar barnacle	Plicate barnacle	Rock osyter	Ornate limpet	Radiate limpet	Black nerite
Site A	Total number of animals	308	46	78	386	0	63	47	55
	Mean Animals per 1 m^2	39	6	10	48	0	8	6	7
Site B	Total number of animals	52	15	427	85	49	50	96	29
	Mean Animals per 1 m^2	7	2	53	11	6	6	12	4

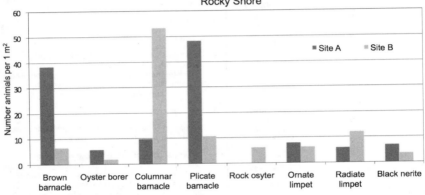

Number of Rock Based Animals per 1 m^2 of Rocky Shore

3. (a) **Heavy rainfall** or inflow of floodwater from nearby river channels may cause a decline in conductivity.
   (b) **Evaporation** from the lake concentrates salts and the conductivity will increase.

4. Physical gradients will govern what species will be found and where in a particular area, as determined by their specific tolerances to abiotic factors.

Vertical Distribution in a Lake Community
(page 293)
1. (a) Zooplankton are restricted to the surface waters of the lake during the warmer months, but are distributed throughout the water column in the cooler months.
   (b) Oxygen levels in the water.
   (c) Abiotic

2. *Daphnia* migrate to deeper (=darker) water during the day and move to surface waters at night. The graph of predation rate at different light intensities shows that golden shiners have poor capture rates at low light intensities. It is therefore likely that *Daphnia* migrates to remain in regions of low light and avoid being eaten.

3. Student's own discussion. Use the following points to construct your answer:
   – Abiotic factors (light, dissolved oxygen, temperature) in a lake can change seasonally. The vertical distribution of organisms will change as these

factors change.
   – An organism's tolerance for changes in abiotic factors will determine the limits of its vertical distribution patterns.
   – The presence of a predator can influence vertical distribution. Prey will adopt behaviors to limit predation, e.g. by migrating in the water column.

Plants as Producers (page 295)
1. (a) water + carbon dioxide (in the presence of light and chlorophyll) → glucose + oxygen + water
   (b) $12H_2O + 6CO_2 \rightarrow C_6H_{12}O_6 + 6O_2 + 6H_2O$

2. Importance of photosynthesis (in any order):
   (a) Transforms light energy into chemical energy available to food chains.
   (b) Creates organic molecules used as building blocks for creating more complex molecules.
   (c) Releases free oxygen into the atmosphere; required by many other life forms.

3. Algae are producers and need to remain in the euphotic zone; the zone where there is enough light penetration for photosynthesis to occur (0-30 m).

4. Any of: Oxygen becomes in shorter supply. CO_2 levels in the atmosphere build up with fewer plants around to act as carbon sinks. Climate warms progressively.

Modes of Nutrition (page 296)

1. Both photoautotrophs and chemoautotrophs are organisms that produce their own 'food' (organic compounds) from inorganic sources. Photoautotrophs use light as an energy source to synthesise organic compounds, using carbon dioxide as a carbon source. Chemoautotrophs use organic or inorganic compounds (e.g. sulfide) as an energy source to synthesise organic compounds from carbon dioxide and water. In contrast chemoheterotrophs cannot make organic compounds (food) themselves. They must take in organic sources of carbon, using inorganic or organic compounds as a source of energy (often, both the energy and the carbon source is glucose).

2. **Saprotrophs** (e.g. fungi and decomposer bacteria) live (feed) off dead or decaying matter, whereas **parasites** live in or on living organisms from which they derive nutrients and shelter.

Food Chains (page 297)

1. (a) The sun.
   (b) Refer to the diagram, below

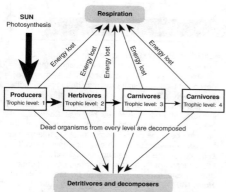

Some secondary consumers feed directly off decomposer organisms

2. (a) Each successive trophic level has less energy.
   (b) Energy is lost by respiration as it is passed from one trophic level to the next.

3. The kingfisher occupies trophic level 3 or 4 at different times (depending on the prey of choice).

Constructing a Food Web (page 298)

1. Some food chain examples as below (there are others)
   (a) Algae → zooplankton → diving beetle
   (b) Algae → zooplankton → stickleback → pike
   (c) Macrophyte → great pond snail → herbivorous water beetle → stickleback → pike
   (d) Macrophyte → carp → pike
   (e) Algae → mosquito larva → Hydra → dragonfly larva → carp → pike
   (f) Macrophyte → herbivorous water beetle → carp → pike
   (g) Algae → zooplankton → Asplanchna → leech → dragonfly larva → carp → pike
   (h) Detritus → Paramecium → Asplanchna → leech → dragonfly larva → carp → pike
   (i) Detritus → great pond snail → leech → dragonfly larva → carp → pike
   (j) Detritus → Paramecium → mosquito larva → Hydra → dragonfly larva → carp → pike

2. See diagram below.

Cave Food Webs (page 300)

1. Cave food web: Diagram at the top of the next page.

2. The major level missing from the cave food web is the producer level.

3. Energy is imported into the cave ecosystem in the form of guano (droppings) from organisms that enter the cave (either briefly or to roost). Rotting vegetation etc. may also enter by being washed in from outside.

4. Energy may be removed by organisms leaving the cave and/or dying outside it or by material being carried out of the system by the stream.

5. The amount of guano in the cave would decline. If there was enough of a decline in guano production there would not be enough energy to support all the

Constructing a lake foodweb:

For reasons of space, the names have been omitted from this solution but the relative positions of each organism is as presented in the workbook. Trophic levels are indicated by the letter T and the number(s) of the level(s) occupied. Note: the trophic level a species occupies will depend on the trophic position of its food items. For example, the carp occupies several different trophic levels, since it feeds on macrophytes, and on both primary and tertiary consumers. The tertiary consumers that the carp eats will also be feeding at a number of different levels, hence the complexity of food webs and the difficulty in accurately representing them in diagrams.

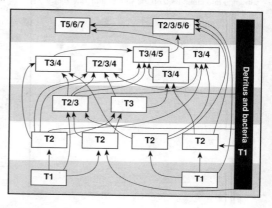

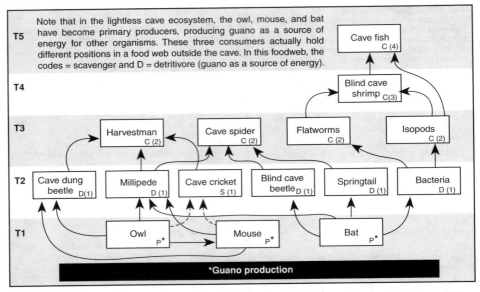

T5 Note that in the lightless cave ecosystem, the owl, mouse, and bat have become primary producers, producing guano as a source of energy for other organisms. These three consumers actually hold different positions in a food web outside the cave. In this foodweb, the codes = scavenger and D = detritivore (guano as a source of energy).

Cave fish C (4)

T4 Blind cave shrimp C(3)

T3 Harvestman C (2) | Cave spider C (2) | Flatworms C (2) | Isopods C (2)

T2 Cave dung beetle D(1) | Millipede D (1) | Cave cricket S (1) | Blind cave beetle D (1) | Springtail D (1) | Bacteria D (1)

T1 Owl P* | Mouse P* | Bat P*

*Guano production

organisms of the cave food web. Some or all would die and the food web or parts of it would collapse.

The Darkest Depths (page 301)

1. Conditions include extremely high water pressure, extreme temperature gradients, complete darkness, and high dissolved mineral contents in the water.

2. Because the conditions near hydrothermal vents are unique and the organisms living near the vents are so dependent upon the conditions produced in that environment, there is little opportunity for interactions beyond the vent or spreading to new environments.

3. Chemosynthetic bacteria form the basis of the vent community. They are the producers that form the first trophic level upon the which the consumers feed. Tubeworms, mussels and Pompeii worms feed on the bacteria or form mutualistic relationships with them. Shrimps and crabs feed on the worms and mussels and on detritus, while fish and octopi are top predators.

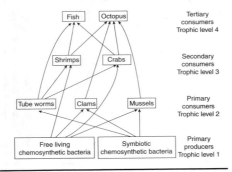

Fish	Octopus	Tertiary consumers Trophic level 4
Shrimps	Crabs	Secondary consumers Trophic level 3
Tube worms	Clams	Mussels	Primary consumers Trophic level 2
Free living chemosynthetic bacteria	Symbiotic chemosynthetic bacteria	Primary producers Trophic level 1

Measuring Primary Productivity (page 302)

1. LAI is an indirect measure of the capacity of the plant to intercept light, photosynthesize, and produce new plant biomass. High LAIs may be typical of high productivity, although this is not necessarily the case. Large trees may support a large biomass with relatively low rates of production of new biomass. Conversely, grasslands may have high rates of production despite cropping because they are not supporting a large, static biomass. The concept is more applicable in agricultural situations where there can be marked **reductions** in the (typical) LAI for a crop, e.g. through crop damage due to pests, and this reduces the primary productivity. **Note**: The LAI is the measure of the leaf area of a plant exposed to incoming light, expressed in relation to the ground surface area beneath the plant.

2. (a) The procedure outlined only gives an estimate of NPP because you cannot easily determine the biomass not collected due to consumption or death.
   (b) To express standing crop in kJ m^{-2} you would need to know the energy content of the plant material (per known mass unit measured, e.g. kg). **Note**: A calorimeter could be used to do this.
   (c) To calculate GPP you would need to know the energy lost in respiration, e.g. by measuring the CO_2 lost at night.

Production and Trophic Efficiency (page 303)

1. Net primary production refers to the net amount of producer biomass available per unit area to the next trophic level. Net primary productivity is the rate of producer biomass production or the producer biomass produced per area per unit time.

2. (a)- (c) and any of the following:
   – Amount and availability of light for photosynthesis. This is higher in the tropics.

- Temperature. Higher temperatures are generally conducive to higher productivity.
- Availability of water. Photosynthesis (and therefore productivity) will be limited when water is scarce.
- Availability of nutrients. Nutrient limitations will limit plant growth and lower productivity.

3. (a)-(c) any of the following:
   - High diversity of grassland species contributing to ecosystem efficiencies (different tolerances and preferences so photosynthesis is maximized).
   - High root production typical of herbaceous species.
   - High producer turnover because continual cropping by herbivores keeps plants actively growing.
   - High rates of nutrient recycling so nutrient availability is not a factor in limiting productivity.
   - Savanna occurs in equatorial or near equatorial latitudes so high light and temperature help to increase rates of plant photosynthesis.
   - Continual supplies of nutrient from the dung of primary consumers (grazing herbivores).

4. (a) The key factors limiting rates of primary production in **terrestrial** ecosystems are temperature and moisture; the productivity of tundra ecosystems is limited by low temperatures, while that of desert ecosystems is limited by moisture availability. Tropical rainforest ecosystems do not have these same limitations.
   (b) In aquatic systems, light and nutrient availability limit rates of production. The NPP of open ocean is low relative to coastal systems because of the low levels of nutrients. Nitrogen and phosphorus, in particular, are very low in the open ocean but higher in coastal systems which receive inputs from the land. **Note**: Although light may be limiting to productivity in the open ocean, tropical waters are less productive than one would predict from the higher light intensities there; low nutrient availability is the critical factor in this case.

5. (a) NPP of a particular crop can be maximized by reducing losses to pests, spraying to reduce losses to disease, maximizing light penetration and nutrient uptake by keeping competing plants to a minimum, ensuring adequate amounts of water and nutrients.
   (b) Livestock productivities can be maximized using the same principles: minimizing levels of disease and ensuring optimum nutrition, optimizing stocking densities to reduce stress, reducing energy losses by restricting excessive movement (smaller paddocks) and providing shelter belts or indoor housing in colder weather.

6. Deserts are often high light environments, but are limited by water and nutrient availability so productivities are low. Intensive horticultural land is provided with plentiful water and nutrients and crops are often kept in climate controlled environments to maximise temperatures and raise carbon dioxide levels. The result is very high productivities (maintained by continual high inputs of energy and matter).

Quantifying Energy Flow in an Ecosystem
(page 305)
1. (a) 14,000   (b) 180   (c) 35   (d) 100

2. Solar energy

3. A. Photosynthesis
   B. Eating/feeding/ingestion
   C. Respiration
   D. Export (lost from this ecosystem to another)
   E. Decomposers and detritivores feeding on other decomposers and detritivores
   F. Radiation of heat to the atmosphere
   G. Excretion/egestion/death

4. (a) 1,700,000 ÷ 7,000,000 x 100 = 24.28%
   (b) It is reflected. Plants appear green because those wavelengths are not absorbed. Reflected light falls on other objects as well as back into space.

5. (a) 87,400 ÷ 1,700,000 x 100 = 5.14%
   (b) 1,700,000 - 87,400 = 1,612,600 (94.86%)
   (c) Most of the energy absorbed by producers is **not** used in photosynthesis. This excess energy, which is not fixed, is lost as heat (although the heat loss component **before** the producer level is not usually shown on energy flow diagrams). **Note**: Some of the light energy absorbed through accessory pigments such as carotenoids widens the spectrum that can drive photosynthesis. However, much of accessory pigment activity is associated with photoprotection; they absorb and dissipate excess light energy that would otherwise damage chlorophyll.

6. (a) 78,835 kJ
   (b) 78,835 ÷ 1,700,000 x 100 = 4.64%

7. (a) Decomposers and detritivores
   (b) Transport by wind or water to another ecosystem (e.g. blown or carried in water currents).

8. (a) Low oxygen or anaerobic, low temperature, low moisture.
   (b) Energy remains locked up in the detrital material and is not released.
   (c) Geological reservoir:

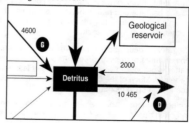

   (d) **Oil** (petroleum) and **natural gas**, formed from the remains of marine plankton. **Coal** and **peat** are both of plant origin; peat is partly decomposed, and coal is fossilized.

9. (a) 87,400 → 14,000:   14,000 ÷ 87,400 x 100 = 16%
   (b) 14,000 → 1600:   1600 ÷14,000 x 100 = 11.4%
   (c) 1600 → 90:   90 ÷ 1600 x 100 = 5.6%

Ecological Pyramids (page 307)
1. (a) Number pyramid: Numbers of individual organisms at each trophic level.
   (b) Biomass pyramid: Weight (usually dry weight) of all organisms at each trophic level.
   (c) Energy pyramid: Energy content of all organisms at each trophic level.

2. Biomass or energy pyramids usually more accurately reflect the energy available to the next trophic level than pyramids of numbers. Pyramids of numbers can be misleading because a small number of producers may represent a large amount of biomass or energy.

3. Producers include the large trees. These have a large biomass and energy content per individual.

4. (a) 8690 → 142 = 8548 kJ = 1.6%
   (b) 142 → 12 = 130 kJ = 8.5%
   (c) Energy passed on from producers to primary consumers is less than the expected 10% because a lot of energy is diverted to the decomposers.
   (d) Decomposers
   (e) In a plankton community, turnover times (generation times of organisms) are very short and there is a lot of dead material both in the water and on the bottom. This provides a rich energy source to support a large biomass of decomposers.

5. The algae are reproducing at a high rate, but are being heavily cropped by the larger biomass of zooplankton.

Nutrient Cycles (page 309)

1. (a) Bacteria are able to make conversions to and from elements and their ionic states. This gives plants and animals access to nutrients that they would otherwise not have (i.e. increases bioavailability).
   (b) Fungi decompose organic matter, returning nutrients to the soil where plants and bacteria can access them. They are also able to convert some nutrients into more readily accessible forms.
   (c) Plants are able make their own food and, when they die, add this to the soil in the form of nutrients that can be broken down and used by bacteria and fungi. They also provide browsing animals with nutrients when they are eaten.
   (d) Animals break down materials from plants, fungi and bacteria and return then to the soil with their wastes and when they die allowing the nutrients in them to re-enter the cycle.

2. The rates of decomposition are very high in the higher temperatures of tropical forests. As a result, decaying matter is processed very quickly and very little remains in the soil. Much of the carbon and other nutrients are also locked up in biomass.

3. A macronutrient is one that is required in large amounts and often needs to be replaced on a regular basis by eating or drinking. They are often needed for growth and repair of the organism. Micronutrients (trace elements) are needed in much smaller amounts and may not need to be replaced very often. However they are often essential to the efficient operation of sensitive biochemical pathways (e.g. as enzyme cofactors).

The Hydrologic Cycle (page 310)

1. (a) Surface runoff   (b) Ground-water flow

2. (a)-(c) any of the following, in any order:
   - Humans withdraw water from ground-water storage, rivers, and lakes. It may be used to supply domestic or personal use, or for irrigation. Consequently it may become depleted in specific areas or its normal destination altered.
   - Humans divert water and alter natural flows through damming and controlled flows. This alters the normal balance of seasonal water movements.
   - Humans may use water courses or water bodies for disposal of waste, polluting it and making it unsuitable for other organisms.
   - Humans clear vegetation, reducing the amount of water re-entering the atmosphere and being returned to the land via precipitation.

3. The oceans

4. In descending order of magnitude: Snow and ice (in ice sheets and glaciers), ground-water, lakes, soil, atmosphere, rivers.

5. Plants lose a lot of water through transpiration. This is returned to the atmosphere where it condenses and then precipitates back to the land.

The Carbon Cycle (page 311)

1. Arrows can be added for the points (a)-(d) as follows:
   (a) Dissolving of limestone by acid rain: Arrow from the limestone layer to atmospheric CO_2.
   (b) Release of carbon from the marine food chain: Arrows (labelled **respiration**) from marine organisms (shark, algae, fish) to atmospheric CO_2.
   (c) Mining and burning of coal: Arrow from the coal seam to atmospheric CO_2.
   (d) Burning of plant material: Arrow (labelled **combustion**) from the trees and/or grassland to atmospheric CO_2.

2. (a) Coal: Plant material trapped under sediment in swampy conditions millions of years ago.
   (b) Oil: Marine plankton rapidly buried in sediment mya.
   (c) Limestone (also chalk = fine limestone): Shells of molluscs, skeletons of coral and other marine organisms with skeletons of calcium carbonate piled upon seabeds and compressed.

3. (a) **Respiration** (stepwise oxidation of glucose) and **combustion** (rapid oxidation of organic substances accompanied by heat).
   (b) Both involve the release of CO_2.

4. (a) - (d) in any order: Atmosphere, coal, limestone, and oil and natural gas.

5. (a) Photosynthesis   (b) Respiration

6. Carbon would eventually be locked up in the bodies (remains) of dead organisms. Dead matter would not rot. Possible gradual loss of CO_2 from the atmosphere.

7. (a) Dung beetles: Bury the cow manure and the larvae feed on it. Burying the dung makes it available to decomposers in the soil. The beetle larvae reprocess the dung, using it as a food source. It therefore re-enters the trophic system.
   (b) Termites: Digest the cellulose in plant material, breaking it down and freeing up the carbon back into the ecosystem.
   (c) Fungi: Break down dead material, utilizing it as food and converting it into the fungal body. This makes it available to re-enter the food chain.

8. Many insects play roles in the digestion of cellulose and animal wastes. Termites use bacteria in their gut to digest cellulose from woody trees. Beetles may eat animal waste or lay eggs on it so their grubs may use it as a food source.

9. (a) Humans deplete these fossil fuel reserves through mining (fossil fuels provide readily available energy).
(b) The burning of fossil fuels increases the amount of carbon dioxide in the atmosphere, contributing to the rise in global temperatures. Burning also increases levels of air pollution.
(c) Minimizing fossil fuels use through the use of alternative, environmentally clean sources of energy (solar energy, wind energy). Making sure that when fossil fuels are burnt, that combustion is as clean (complete) as possible, to minimize pollution.

The Nitrogen Cycle (page 313)

1. (a)-(e) any of the following in any order:
   - Decomposition or decay of dead organisms, to ammonia by decomposer bacteria (ammonification).
   - Nitrification of ammonium ions to nitrite by nitrifying bacteria such as *Nitrosomonas* ($NH_4^+ \rightarrow NO_2^-$)
   - Nitrification of nitrite to nitrate by nitrifying bacteria such as *Nitrobacter* ($NO_2^- \rightarrow NO_3^-$)
   - Denitrification of nitrate to nitrogen gas by anaerobic denitrifying bacteria such as *Pseudomonas* ($NO_3^- \rightarrow N_{2(g)}$)
   - Fixation of atmospheric nitrogen to nitrate by nitrogen fixing bacteria such as *Azotobacter* and *Rhizobium* ($N_2 \rightarrow NO_3^-$)
   - Fixation of atmospheric nitrogen to ammonia by nitrogen fixing cyanobacteria ($N_2 \rightarrow NH_3$)

2. (a) Oxidation of atmospheric nitrogen by lightning.
   (b) Nitrogen fixation (by bacteria).
   (c) Production of nitrogen fertilizer through the Haber process.

3. Denitrification

4. The atmosphere.

5. Nitrate.

6. Any one of: amino acids, proteins, chlorophyll.

7. Animals ingest food (plants or other animals); they are heterotrophic.

8. Leguminous material is high in nitrogen. Plowing it in replenishes soil nitrogen and reduces the need for additional nitrogen fertilizer when growing non-leguminous crops subsequently.

9. Human intervention in the nitrogen cycle by (a)-(e) any of the following in any order):
   - Addition of nitrogen fertilizers to the land. This practice supplies inorganic nitrogen, as nitrate, for plant growth, but has the disadvantage that any excess nitrogen, not absorbed by plants, may enter and pollute ground water and water bodies.
   - Industrial physical-chemical fixation of nitrogen (through the Haber process) combines hydrogen and nitrogen to ammonia, which can be used to manufacture inorganic nitrogen fertilizers. This is an industrial process, which requires high temperatures and pressures and uses a large amount of energy. The effects of applied inorganic nitrogen are outlined in (a) above.
   - Genetic modification of crop plants so that they can fix nitrogen. The effect of this is to increase the range of crop plants capable of growing on nitrogen deficient soils. Potentially, this could make a beneficial contribution to soil fertility.
   - Large-scale, assisted composting produces nitrogen rich organic fertilizer which has the effect of improving soil fertility and structure. This has beneficial effects in reducing the amount of inorganic nitrogen fertilizer that must be applied.
   - Burning and harvesting removes nitrogen from the land and releases nitrogen oxides into the atmosphere.
   - Discharge of effluent (particular animal waste) into waterways enriches water bodies and leads to localized pollution and eutrophication.
   - Irrigation can accelerate loss of nitrate from the soil by increasing the rate at which nitrates are washed out of the soil into ground water.

Nitrogen Pollution (page 315)

1. (a) NO contributes to the formation of low level ozone which is a constituent of photochemical smog
   (b) N_2O depletes ozone in the upper atmosphere
   (c) NO_2 is a toxic inhalant. It also contributes to the formation of nitric acid in the atmosphere and therefore acid rain.
   (d) NO_3^- is a water pollutant. It causes eutrophication, the accelerated growth of algae in waterways, and can cause severe health problems if drinking water contains significant amounts.

2. NO persists in the atmosphere both causing and being released by cyclic chemical reactions. NO reacts with oxygen to form toxic NO_2, which reacts with water to form HNO_3 (acid rain) and HNO_2. The HNO_2 decomposes, releasing NO to react again. NO will continue this cycling until it reacts with a chemical that removes it from the cycle.

3. Even after nitrogen fertilizers are not used, there is a large nitrogen load in soil and groundwater. Groundwater may take many years to move from its point of origin to its point of exit. Nitrate fertilizers that leach into groundwater now will move with this ground water and exit into waterways many years afterwards. In some cases, the lag may be up to fifty years.

4. (a) 1860: reactive N deposition in the ocean = 156.5 million tonnes. Release of unreactive nitrogen = 301 million tonnes.
   1995: reactive N deposition in the ocean = 202 million tonnes. Release of unreactive nitrogen = 322 million tonnes. This is an increase of 45.5 million tonnes of reactive N deposition but an increase of only 21 million tonnes of unreactive nitrogen released Result: twice as much reactive nitrogen has been added to the ocean than has been released as unreactive nitrogen.
   (b) Algal blooms are becoming more common in the oceans as nitrate levels slowly rise. Many of these blooms are algae that contain small amounts of toxins. These can be concentrated by filter feeders such as mussels and if eaten can cause poisoning.

5. (a) Nitrates are highly soluble in water and a lot is rapidly washed away or leached from the soil and not incorporated into plant tissues. Nitrates are also broken down by bacteria and returned to the air. Some nitrates will accumulate in the soil over time but not be accessible to plants. All these factors contribute to "lost" nitrogen.
   (b) Nitrogen losses could be minimized by fertilizer application at appropriate times and rates, and by

sensible irrigation practices. Using slow release fertilizers in times of frequent rain also slows down the rate at which nitrates are lost into groundwater.

KEY TERMS: Mix and Match (page 317)

autotroph (E), carbon cycle (A), chemoautotroph (F), consumer (M), decomposer (I), detritivore (G), ecological pyramid (W), food chain (D), food web (Q), gross primary production (V), heterotroph (N), hydrologic cycle (H), net primary production (K), nitrogen cycle (C), nutrient cycle (S), photoautotroph (L), primary consumer (U), producer (B), primary productivity (P), saprotroph (R), ten percent rule (T), trophic efficiency (J), trophic level (O).

Features of Populations (page 319)

1. (a) One of the following:
   Population growth rate: If this increases (or decreases) from one time interval to the next, it indicates that the population is probably also increasing (or decreasing). **Note**: The **intrinsic** rate of population increase (r_{max}) should be distinguished from population growth rates that account for the increasing number of individuals in the population (rN). The intrinsic population growth rate is a characteristic value for each species but rN can increase rapidly as more and more individuals add to the population increase (giving an exponential curve). Population growth rates account for birth and death rates but do not usually account for losses and gains through migration, which are usually assumed to be equal.
   Total abundance: If this increases (or decreases) from one time interval to the next, it indicates that the population is also increasing (or decreasing).
   Mortality rate: If this is increasing from one time interval to the next, it indicates that the population may be decreasing (you must also account for other sources of population change).
   Birth rate & population fertility: If these increase from one time interval to the next, they indicate that the population may be increasing (you must also account for other sources of population change).
   Age structure: A population dominated by young individuals is usually increasing. A population dominated by old (especially post-reproductive) individuals is usually decreasing.
   (b) One of the following:
   Distribution: A very clumped distribution may indicate that only some parts of the environment are suitable for supporting individuals.
   Population growth and birth *rates*: If these are low or declining it may indicate an inability of the environment to support the population density.
   Mortality rates: If these are very high or increasing it *may* indicate an inability of the environment to support the present population density.

2. (a) **Measurable attributes**: Density, distribution, total abundance, sex ratios, migration (sometimes difficult). In some cases, depending on the organism, also age structure and population fertility.
   (b) **Calculated attributes**: Population growth rate, natality (birth rate) and mortality (death rate).

3. (a) Population sampling of an endangered species allows us to determine (any of): How fast a population is growing (if at all); the age and sex

structure of the population (i.e. is it dominated by young or very old, non-reproductive, individuals); population abundance, density and distribution in different areas (indicating habitat preference and suitability); sources of mortality (predation, disease, starvation etc.); population fertility (reproductive state). This type of information allows informed decisions to be made about the current status of the population and how best to manage it (through habitat restoration or captive breeding for example).
   (b) Population sampling of a managed fish species allows us to determine the population growth rate. This is critical to establishing the level of fishing that can be supported by the population (the sustainable harvest) without irreversible population decline. The growth rate is calculated taking into account population abundance, and birth and death rates. Sustainable harvest can be built into the equation as one of the (controllable) sources of mortality.

Density and Distribution (page 320)

1. (a) Resources such as food and shelter are not usually spread through the environment in an even manner. Organisms will clump around these resources.
   (b) Some organisms group together for protection from the physical environment or from predators. They may also group together for mating and reproduction. Clumped distributions may also result from the method of dispersal (e.g. in plants, vegetative spread (as opposed to dispersal by seeds) leads to clumping around the parent plant).

2. Territorial behavior.

3. Resources in the environment are limited but are distributed uniformly.

4. (a) **Clumped**: Many marine gastropods, colonial birds (seasonally), many mammals that exhibit grouping/ herd behavior, schooling fish, colonial insects, many other invertebrates such as coral, some plants with limited dispersal.
   (b) **Random**: Weed plants with effective dispersal method, shellfish on sand or mud substrate.
   (c) **Uniform**: Territorial organisms, monoculture plantings (e.g. crops, timber plantations).

Population Age Structure (page 321)

1. (a) 3:1
   (b) Other factors besides changes in age structure can affect population growth, e.g. sex ratios, population fertility, and migration.

2. Over a short duration, the large cohort of pre-reproductive individuals will reach reproductive age and the population will continue to grow. Even if the rate of population growth continues to slow it will take several generations before the 'bulge' of reproductive individuals moves into the post-reproductive phase.

3. (a) Mortality
   (b) Higher proportion of smaller/younger fish.

4. (a) 3 years   (b) 5 years   (c) 8 years

5. (a) Gray face: It has palms of all sizes and therefore all ages are represented.
   (b) Golf course: No young plants are represented.

6. The population will age, with the established palms growing taller, and no new palms becoming established. Eventually these older palms will die with no replacement (unless there is a planting program).

7. Not all organisms (e.g. plants, fish) grow at the same rate. Size may depend on the quality and quantity of food supply. Some seasons may produce more growth than others.

8. If the age structure in the short-medium term shows a trend to smaller/younger age classes, then harvesting pressure is too severe. If this continues, there will be few individuals of reproductive age and, consequently, a decline in the harvestable stock (population size).

Life Tables and Survivorship (page 323)

1. (a) The majority of deaths occur in the first year.
   (b) Type III (early loss).

2. (a) See graph below:

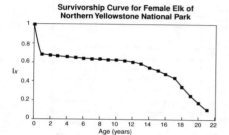

Survivorship Curve for Female Elk of Northern Yellowstone National Park

(x-axis: Age (years), y-axis: l_x)

(b) High mortality in the first year of life then very low mortality for the next twelve years before high mortality in old age (13 years old and onwards). This is a modified Type I (late loss).

3. Biologists use life table data to determine when the greatest mortality occurs, for example, in endangered or managed/exploited populations. Determining the timing of greatest mortality can help to establish the causes of mortality and enable conservation/management measures to be introduced appropriately. For example, in the case of exploited populations, restrictions on the age/size at harvest can enable adequate recruitment into adult life stages to offset population declines. In the case of endangered species, identifying causes of mortality enables more cost-effective population management (i.e. intensive management at specific, vulnerable life stages).

Survivorship Curves (page 324)

1. In some undeveloped countries, with high reproductive rates but poor infant survival, the curve may resemble a modified Type III curve. Even though there is parental care, this does not offset the losses of young to starvation and disease.

2. They produce vast quantities of eggs/offspring.

3. Well developed, often prolonged, parental care.

4. This statement is realistic because particular patterns of survivorship are hypothetical and only provide a tool for categorizing the characteristics of populations. The survivorship curves of many species may show a mix of Type I, II, and III characteristics depending on the life cycle stage. Many extrinsic factors may also influence mortality and it is not necessarily possible to accurately predict a steady-state pattern of survivorship for any one species.

Survivorship and Life Expectancy (page 325)

1. Life expectancy is a measure of the number of years a person is expected to live for at any give age. It is based on the probability of living to the next year of life. Different stages of life leave people more vulnerable than others, so life expectancy changes as one moves through these areas of life. A new born baby is highly vulnerable and has a lower life expectancy than a one year old. An 80 year is also vulnerable and has a low life expectancy. However a 90 year has a relatively high life expectancy as people who reach this age tend to then live a number of years longer.

2. As GDP increases so too does the life expectancy of the population. The curve levels out at a GDP of around 30,000 US dollars per capita.

3. Infant mortality rate is linked to a country's GDP because wealthy countries tend to have better medical support and public health infrastructure than poorer countries. This means that even infants with serious medical problems at birth are more likely to survive due the care they are likely to receive. Better education of parents and better infant nutrition are also factors in the survival of infants in high GDP countries.

4. Countries vary markedly in their living conditions and quality of life. These are two major factors in determining he survivorship of people. Countries where war and sanitation are problems have lower survivorship of their citizens.

5. (a) 78   (b) 70   (c) 63

Population Growth (page 326)

1. (a) Mortality: Number of individuals dying per unit time (death rate).
   (b) Natality: Number of individuals born per unit time (birth rate).
   (c) Net migration rate: Net change in population size per unit time due to immigration and emigration.

2. Population growth will be constrained to a level that can be sustained by the factor that is most limiting.

3. (b) A declining population: $B + I < D + E$
   (c) An increasing population: $B + I > D + E$

4. (a) Birth rate = 14 births ÷ 100 total number of individuals x 100 % = 14% per year
   (b) Net migration rate = 2% per year
   (c) Death rate = 20% per year
   (d) Rate of population change: birth rate − death rate + net migration rate = 14 − 20 + 2 = −4% per year
   (e) The population is **declining**.

5. Limiting factors to human population growth: availability of food or land (to live or grow food), prevalence of disease and ability of public health system to prevent and treat it.

Patterns of Population Growth (page 327)

1. As population numbers increase, the resistance of the environment (to further population increase) increases. This constrains the population to keep to a size that the environment can support at any one time.

2. Environmental resistance refers to all the limiting factors that together act to prevent further population increase (achievement of biotic potential, r_{max}).

3. (a) The maximum population size (of a species) that can be supported by the environment.
   (b) Carrying capacity limits population growth because as the population size increases, population growth slows (when N = K population growth stops). **Note:** For those interested in extension in this area, the effect of K on population growth is defined by the mathematical expression of logistic growth. This is covered in many, more advanced, biology texts.

4. (a) A new introduction increases exponentially (or nearly so) in that environment is unexploited up to that point. Resources (food, space, shelter etc.) are plentiful and readily available. The population rapidly increases, then slows as the population encounters environmental resistance.
   (b) Population numbers would fluctuate around some relatively stable population size that equates to what the environment can support (the carrying capacity).

5. Introduced grazing species can lower the carrying capacity of environments by reducing the ability of the environment to recover from the impacts of grazing. **Note:** High population numbers and high stocking levels lead to overgrazing, soil loss, proliferation of weeds and loss of desirable plant species. Native consumers have patterns of resource use and population growth that do not result in over-exploitation.

r and K Selection (page 328)

1. *r* selected species predominate in early successional communities because the are opportunistic generalists able to thrive in variable, unstable environments where abiotic factors are relatively more influential than biotic interactions. *r*-selected species can rapidly colonize new environments because they reproduce rapidly.

2. K selected species predominate in the relatively more predictable environments of climax communities. This is because they usually have a specialist niche, and make efficient use of available resources available.

3. – K-selected species exist near the carrying capacity of the environment and are slow to adapt to change. A catastrophic event (e.g. drought, fire, landslide) can destroy a climax community and create a successional environment in which *r*-selected species would predominate over K-selected species.
   – K-selected species are specialized to reduce competition. The introduction of a new K-selected species with similar resource requirements will alter the competitive balance and probably also the composition of the climax community.

Human Demography (page 329)

Page 1 (apologies for numbering error in this activity)

1. Diagram C corresponds to stage one of the DTM. The wide base of the pyramid indicates a large number of under 15s (pre-reproductive) but the sides of the pyramid are steep and not many live to old age, so death rates are high. The combination of high birth rates (many children) and high death rates means the population numbers are largely stationary.

2. In less economically developed nations (LEDN), children are required to contribute to the household economy by helping with work and raising younger siblings. In more economically developed nations (MEDN), the household income is more likely to come from outside industry (i.e. wage and salary earning rather than farming, herding animals, or making crafts) so extra children become a cost to the household rather than contributors in their own right. This is especially the case because the costs of child rearing (education, clothing, transport etc) are higher in MEDN.

Page 2

1. (a) and (b) see tables below.

Age	Males Pre-1950 No. of deaths	Males Pre-1950 Survivorship	Females Pre-1950 No. of deaths	Females Pre-1950 Survivorship
0-9	5	30	7	30
10-19	1	25	2	23
20-29	4	24	2	21
30-39	2	20	1	19
40-49	4	18	3	18
50-59	2	14	3	15
60-69	3	12	7	13
70-79	7	9	4	6
80-89	2	2	2	2
90-99	0	0	0	0
Total	30		30	

Age	Males Post 1950 No. of deaths	Males Post 1950 Survivorship	Females Post-1950 No. of deaths	Females Post-1950 Survivorship
0-9	1	30	0	30
10-19	1	29	0	30
20-29	0	28	0	30
30-39	2	28	1	30
40-49	3	26	2	29
50-59	1	23	4	27
60-69	5	22	4	23
70-79	7	17	4	19
80-89	8	10	10	15
90-99	2	2	5	5
Total	30		30	

2. (a)

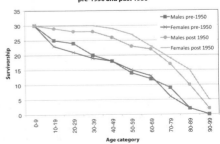

Survivorship for males and females in the US pre-1950 and post 1950

(b) Survivorship for both males and females has improved since 1950.

(c) The pre-1950s had two world wars in which many young men were killed. Diseases such as TB and polio also killed many people at a young age. In contrast, many medical advancements have been made in the decades since 1950, these have increased life expectancy. There has also been less global conflict (fewer young men dying in war).

World Population Growth (page 331)

1. (a) Africa
   (b) Poor education on family planning. Entrenched cultural practices (large families are desirable).

2. The increased mechanization of agriculture and move away from subsistence farming has reduced the need for large numbers of rural workers and encouraged the move of people to cities.

3. (a) Advantages of urbanization include: More job opportunities, better housing, more reliable food supply, freedom from village traditions, chance to learn skills, more opportunity to make money.
   (b) Problems of urbanization include:
   – problems with adequate provision of food, water, sanitation, housing, jobs, and basic services (such as health care and education).
   – the rapid and unplanned growth of slum or squatter areas that develop on the fringes of cities. These areas often grow rapidly in response to immigrant influxes.
   – increased levels of pollution as a direct or indirect result of increased population pressure.
   – rapid spread of diseases through high density and/or improperly serviced areas.
   – increased crime, particularly in high density, impoverished parts of cities.

The Rise and Fall of Human Populations (page 333)

1. The trend is of continual (close to exponential) growth in the human population.

2. The human population has grown because of increased crop yields and better medical treatment. This has led to a higher standard of living, better nutrition, and a lower mortality rate.

3. Local resources at Tikal and Easter Island were both used to support population growth. When these resources were over exploited, the populations crashed and the lands were abandoned. The early history of these examples tends to mirror what appears to be currently happening on a global scale. This helps us understand the effects of depleted resources on populations whose livelihoods are based on those resources and what can be done to prevent similar events happening again.

Population Regulation (page 334)

1. **Density dependent factors**, such as disease, parasitic infestation, competition, and predation have an increasing effect on population growth as the density of the population increases; their effects are exacerbated at high population densities because they are driven in part by the number of organisms present. **Density**

independent factors, such as flood, fire, and drought have a controlling effect on population size and growth that is independent of the population density. The severity of the impact on the population is not correlated with the density of the population.

2. When population density is low, individuals are well spaced apart. This can reduce stress between individuals (improving the resistance to diseases) as well as making the transmission of the pathogen more difficult. Crowded populations are more susceptible to epidemics of infectious disease.

3. (a) Density dependent factor: Predation (e.g. by ladybird beetles), competition with other aphids for position on the best part of the plant to feed.
   (b) Density independent factor: Temperature (drop in temperature in autumn months in cooler climates causes the population to crash).

Species Interactions (page 335)

1. Savannah:

Interaction	Zebra	Species B
Competition	–	Male rival (–)
Parasitism	–	Tick (–)
Predation	–	Lion (+)

Redwood forest:

Interaction	Redwood	Species B
Competition	–	Redwood (–)
Commensalism	0	Marbled murrelet (+)
Predation (herbivory)	–	Bear (+)
Mutualism	+	Fungi (+)

2. Interactions:

	B	Description
(a)	+	Both species benefit.
(b)	0	Species A benefits, no effect on species B.
(c)	+	Species A (the host) is harmed, species B (the parasite) benefits.
(d)	+	Species A (prey) is harmed, species B (the predator) benefits.
(e)	–	Both species (competitors) are harmed.

3. Predators kill and eat their prey. Parasites feed of their host but do not usually cause the death of the host.

4. Competition may require energy input from both parties (e.g. fighting for mates). More importantly, it reduces access to and availability of resources (e.g. food) for both parties (given that resources are limited).

5. Trees can only grow where sufficient light, nutrients, and water are available. Redwood density is therefore limited by the light available and the restrictions of root competition between neighboring plants. Trees growing too close together will shade each other and compete for nutrients and water, reducing each individual's growth. Trees will be spaced in a way that allows the growth requirements of all individuals to be met.

6. Redwoods depend on a mutualistic relationship with mycorrhizae and their growth is poor without them. Redwoods will only expand into regions where the requirements for mycorrhizal survival are also met.

7. The marbled murrelet nests in the old growth branches of redwoods, so the number of nests is dependent (at least in part) on the density and range of redwoods.

Fewer old growth trees means fewer potential nesting sites. The decline of the marbled murrelet has been linked to the logging of old growth forests.

8. Bears strip the bark from trees for the sapwood after emerging from hibernation. Their feeding preferences are influenced by the density of tree species. If redwood density is too low, they will select other species (e.g. redwoods are preferred in Northern California, Douglas fir in the Pacific Northwest). In this way, they forage in the most energy-efficient manner (effectively 'prey switching' to feed on most abundant species).

9. The relationship could be called parasitism (although the oxpecker does not live on or in the host) or general exploitation as they feed on a host and cause damage without killing the host.

Interspecific Competition (page 337)

1. The two species have similar niche requirements (similar habitats and foods). Red squirrels once occupied a much larger range than currently. This range has contracted steadily since the introduction of the grays. The circumstantial evidence points to the reds being displaced by the grays.

2. The grays have not completely displaced the reds. In areas of suitable coniferous habitat, the reds have maintained their numbers. In some places the two species coexist. **Teacher's note**: It has been suggested that the reds are primarily coniferous dwellers and extended their range into deciduous woodland habitat in the absence of competition.

Niche Differentiation (page 338)

1. (a) Different species may exploit different microhabitats within the ecosystem (e.g. tree trunks, leaf litter, lower or upper canopy).
   (b) Different species may exploit the same resources but at different times of the day or year.

2. Intraspecific competition is more intense (than interspecific competition) because individuals of the same species (conspecifics) are competing for exactly the same resources in the environment. There is very little, if any, opportunity for niche differentiation.

3. Damselfish might reduce competition by (any of): occupying different positions on the reef, having different activity patterns, occupying different microhabitats (e.g. different coral types), specializing in food types in a restricted area vs generalized feeding over a wider area.

Intraspecific Competition (page 339)

1. (a) **Individual growth rate**: Intraspecific competition may reduce individual growth rate when there are insufficient resources for all individuals (Examples: tadpoles, *Daphnia*, many mammals with large litters). **Note**: Individuals compete for limited resources and growth is limited in those individuals that do not get access to sufficient food.
   (b) **Population growth rate**: Intraspecific competition reduces population growth rate. Examples as above. **Teacher's note**: Competition intensifies with increasing population size and, at carrying capacity, the rate of population increase slows to zero.

(c) **Final population size**: Intraspecific competition will limit population size to a level that can be supported by the carrying capacity of the environment. **Note**: In territorial species, this will be determined by the number of suitable territories that can be supported.

2. (a) They reduce their individual growth rate and take longer to reach the size for metamorphosis.
   (b) Density dependent.
   (c) The results of this tank experiment are unlikely to represent a real situation in that the tank tadpoles are not subject to normal sources of mortality and there is no indication of long term survivability (of the growth retarded tadpoles). **Teacher's note**: At high densities, many tadpoles would fail to reproduce and this would naturally limit population growth (and size) in the longer term.

3. Reduce intensity of intraspecific competition by:
   (a) Establishing hierarchies within a social group to give orderly access to resources.
   (b) Establishing territories to defend the resource within a specified area.

4. (a) Carrying capacity might decline as a result of unfavorable climatic events (drought, flood etc.) or loss of a major primary producer (plant species).
   (b) Final population size would be smaller (relative to what it was when carrying capacity was higher).

5. Territoriality is a common consequence of intraspecific competition in mammals and birds. In any habitat, resources are limited and only those with sufficient resources will be able to breed. This is especially the case with mammals and birds, where the costs of reproduction to the individual are high relative to some other taxa. Although energy must be used to establish and maintain a territory, territoriality is energy efficient in the longer term because the breeding pair gains relatively unchallenged access to resources. As is shown in the territory maps of golden eagles and great tits, territories space individuals apart and reduce intraspecific interactions. Territory size is related to the resources available within the defended area. Larger territories occur where resources are poorer or widely dispersed. As is shown by the great tit example, when territory owners are removed, their areas are quickly occupied by birds previously displaced by competition.

Mark and Recapture Sampling (page 341)

1. Results will vary from group to group for this practical. The actual results are not important, but it should serve as a useful vehicle for discussion of such things as sample size, variation in results between groups, and whether the method is a reliable way to estimate the size of a larger unknown group. Discussion could center around what factors could be altered to make it a more reliable method (e.g. larger sample size, degree of mixing, increasing number of samples taken).

2. **Trout in Norwegian lake**:

Size of 1st sample:	109
Size of 2nd sample:	177
No. marked in 2nd sample:	57
Estimated total population:	109 x 177 / 57 = 338.5

3. (a) Some marked animals may die.
   (b) Not enough time for thorough mixing of marked and unmarked animals.

4. (a) and (b) in any order (any two of):
    - Marking does not affect their survival.
    - Marked & unmarked animals are captured randomly.
    - Marks are not lost.
    - The animals are not territorial (must mix back into the population after release).

5. (a) Any animal that cannot move or is highly territorial (e.g. barnacle, tube worm, many mammals).
    (b) Unable to mix with unmarked portion of the population. Recapture at the same location would simply sample the same animals again.

6. (a)-(c) in any order:
    - Banding: leg bands of different color on birds.
    - Tags: crayfish shell, fish skin, mammal ears.
    - Paint/dye used to paint markings in shell/fur.

7. The scientists obtain information on fish growth to establish the relationship between age and growth. This will help manage the population to prevent overfishing. Tracking also helps to map breeding grounds and migrations so that fish can be protected at critical times in their life histories. In addition to these data, researchers will find out more about the general biology of the cod (e.g. data on feeding), which will help in the long term management and recovery of the fish stock.

Predator–Prey Interactions (page 343)
1. (a) Prey   (d) 2.7 - 3.0 years
    (b) 5   (e) Approximately 1 year
    (c) Oscillation or cycles

2. (a) Shell collecting may have led to a decline in the numbers of triton shells. Since tritons are one of the crown-of-thorn's few predators, this may have caused starfish numbers to increase.
    (b) The tritons have a varied diet and feed on many other species apart from the crown-of-thorns starfish. In addition, tritons have never been common enough to be a major population regulator.

3. They were introduced to an environment ideally suited to their requirements (in terms of habitat, breeding conditions, food available etc.) and they were without the controlling influence of their natural predators.

Population Cycles (page 344)
1. (a) Usually between about 3 and 7 years (especially for pronounced peaks), although sometimes as great as a full 10 year cycle. Note: The peaks often appear to be superimposed or the lynx peaks appear to be ahead of the hare peaks. Remember that the lynx are responding to the earlier peaks in hare abundance.
    (b) The lag is the result of the time it takes for the predator to respond (through increased births) to increases in food supply. Note: Lynx are top predators, with longer reproductive times and generation times than hares. When the hare populations increase there is a considerable time delay (lag) before this increase in available food is translated into higher population growth rates in lynx (birth rates must increase, usually mortality rates must also fall). Likewise, a fall in hare numbers takes some time to be registered by a decline in lynx population growth rate.

2. Hares are the principal food item for lynx in this system; there is little opportunity for prey switching (few alternative prey). The lynx cycles follow those of the hares closely with a similar periodicity.

3. (a) When the supply of palatable food declines, birth rates decline (adults are less well nourished and litters are smaller) and the mortality rate increases (more deaths due to starvation and disease as a result of malnutrition). Note: Population growth rates depend on both birth and death rates: ($r = b - d$). When natality declines and mortality increases, r becomes negative and the population declines.
    (b) High mortality (losses from the population) can be sustained by species such as rodents and lagomorphs as long as they can maintain their intrinsically high birth rates. Declines in palatable food adversely affects their ability to do this.

The Modern Atlantis? (page 348)
1. Kiribati is vulnerable to the effects of global warming because it is very low lying with most areas being only a few metres above sea level.

2. Effects include drought, rising salt levels in ground water and erosion. Impacts include the movement of villages to higher ground, loss of land and historical places, and loss of crops.

3. If relocated, the identity of the i-kiribati may be lost or diluted by the other cultures into which they move. Future generations will be brought up under the influence of other societies, and the i-kiribati may eventually cease to exist as a people or culture, especially if relocated to many different countries.

4. Students own research: General summary may suggest that not all scientists or organizations agree on climate change research because each has a different viewpoint or take on the data.

Primary Succession (page 349)
1. Glacial retreat, exposed slip, new volcanic island.

2. (a) Lichens and bryophytes (mosses and liverworts), as well as some hardy annual herb species, are often the first to colonize bare ground.
    (b) Chemically and physically erode the rock (making the beginnings of a soil) and add nutrients by decay.

3. Climax communities tend to have greater biodiversity and a more complex trophic structure than early successional communities. A greater diversity of community interactions buffers the system against disturbances because there are many more organisms with different ecological roles able to compensate for losses from the system.

Succession on Surtsey Island (page 350)
1. Surtsey was ideal as a study site for primary succession because it was an entirely new island, devoid of any soil, and was isolated from nearby influences (such as already established vegetation or urban settlements) that could accelerate the succession process.

2. Early colonizations were primarily influenced by the

island's location to the south of Iceland, so the northern shores are closest to a land mass. Later colonizations were influenced buy the establishment of a gull colony at the southern end of the colony. The gulls would transport seeds and contribute to soil fertility.

3. (a) 1985.
   (b) Transported by birds.
   (c) 1985. This coincides with the establishment of the gull colony as the gulls were instrumental in dispersing seeds.

Secondary Succession (page 351)

1. **Primary succession** refers to the colonization of regions where there is no preexisting community (e.g. rocky slope, exposed slip, new volcanic island). Changes in the community occur in stages until a climax community is reached. **Secondary succession** follows the interruption of an established climax community (e.g. logging, pasture reverting to bush).

2. Secondary succession proceeds more rapidly than primary succession because, although the land is cleared, there is minimal or no loss of soil or seed stores. Many plants may still be able to grow despite the disturbance and the climax community will reestablish faster because nutrients are already available and seeds already laid down.

3. Student's own account is required. Abiotic and biotic factors interact to shape the community, with the outcome dependent on the species involved and aspects of the physical environment, including altitude and latitude. The following points may be included:
   Examples: Logging, forest fire, landslide, or other catastrophic events such as major storm events.

   Abiotic factors: Light quantity and quality, wind, temperature, humidity, rainfall, soil quality and nutrient availability.

   Biotic factors: Trophic relationships and species interactions such as competition and mutualism.

Wetland Succession (page 352)

1. (a) Low evaporation rates   (b) High rainfall

2. Both these conditions are found at high latitudes and/or high altitudes.

3. Land drainage threatens bog ecosystems because it dries out the soil and allows acid intolerant species to invade and compete with the natural bog species.

4. Sphagnum lowers the pH of the surrounding soil and hampers the establishment of the acid intolerant species typical of swamps and fens. Acid tolerant (bog) species can then become established.

Disturbance and Community Structure
(page 353)

1. High diversity systems have a greater number of biotic interactions operating to buffer them against change (the loss or decline of one component (species) is less likely to affect the entire ecosystem). With a large number of species involved, ecosystem processes, such as nutrient recycling, are more efficient and less inclined to disruption.

2. Keystone species are pivotal to some important ecosystem function such as production of biomass or nutrient recycling. Because their role is disproportionately large, their removal has a similarly disproportionate effect on ecosystem function.

3. (a) Sea otter: One of the favorite delicacies of the otter is the large sea urchin, which in turn feeds on kelp. Without sea otters there would be no kelp forests. The diversity of the sea otter's diet of marine invertebrate herbivores and filter feeders reduces competition between benthic grazers and supports greater diversity in those species.
   (b) Beaver: When beavers build dams innumerable species, many threatened or endangered, benefit. Beaver ponds produce food for fish and other animals as well as creating habitat. Beaver activity is closely tied to the regeneration of quaking aspens. Beavers eat the bark of this (their favorite) tree and, by harvesting the trees, release buds for sucker growth and stand replacement.
   (c) Gray wolf: Wolves, as a keystone predator, are an integral component of the ecosystems to which they belong. The wide range of habitats in which they thrive reflects their adaptability as a species. Their diet includes elk, caribou, moose, deer and other large ungulates, as well as smaller prey. Wolves are sensitive to fluctuations in prey abundance, and the balance between wolves and their prey preserves the ecological balance between large herbivores and available forage.
   (d) Quaking aspen: An aggressive pioneer species that frequently colonizes burned ground. The success of quaking aspen is attributed to its extensive root system, which sends up suckers to produce clones of the parent tree. The open canopies of aspen groves allow a rich and diverse understorey of shrubs, forbs and grasses to feed and shelter a variety of wildlife. A large number of birds and browsing mammals are dependent on aspen stands for survival, especially through winter periods.

4. Humans historically kill off top carnivores when they enter a natural ecosystem and this drastically affects biodiversity and leads to ecological imbalances. For example, wolves were nearly hunted out of existence in the USA and Europe prior to the twentieth century. Following eradication of wolves in Yellowstone National Park in the early 1900s, elk numbers increased markedly, destroying vegetation and driving beavers and other animals from the damaged habitats. The pivotal role of top predators was determined only after ecological research during the last century and, as a consequence, wolves were reintroduced to Yellowstone and Idaho. The return of the wolves has resulted in a return of biodiversity as the ecological balance has been restored.
   Another similar case is the depletion of sea otter populations as a result of the fur trade from the mid 1700s to 1911. Removal of the otters resulted in a population explosion of sea urchins (on which the otters preyed) and destruction of the local kelp forests on which a large variety of smaller animals depended. As the sea otter populations recover following reintroductions to the natural range, populations of abalone and sea urchins are predicted to decline, allowing a recovery of marine plant biomass.

Threats to Biodiversity (page 355)

1. Loss of biodiversity from an ecosystem has a cascade effect to the remaining species. The effects depend very much on the species that disappears (e.g. predator, producer) but, in general, species loss results in altered food chains and food webs, allowing for the proliferation of some species and the demise of others. Other changes include a loss of stability and resilience, and disruption to normal processes, interactions and outcomes, such as nutrient cycling, soil formation, pollination, oxygen production, carbon sequestration and climate regulation.

2. Species diversity refers to the number of different species within an area (species richness), while genetic diversity describes the diversity of genes within a particular species. Biodiversity is defined as the measure of all genes, species, and ecosystems in a region, so both genetic and species diversity are important in determining a region's total biodiversity.

3. Student's own opinion as supported by an explanation. The major threats to biodiversity include: Population growth and resource consumption, over-hunting/commercial exploitation, illegal trading, habitat conversion and sprawl, establishment of exotic and invasive species, environmental degradation/pollution, and global warming.

4. 1 **Tropical Andes**
   The richest and most diverse hotspot where it is home to 20 000 endemic plants and at least 1500 endemic non-fish vertebrates.

   2 **Sundaland**
   Some of the largest islands in the world are found here in Southeast Asia. The second-richest hotspot in endemic plants, and well known for its mammalian fauna, which includes the orangutan.

   3 **Mediterranean basin**
   The site of many ancient and modern civilisations, it is the archetype and largest of the five Mediterranean-climate hotspots (also see nos. 9, 12, 19 and 22). One of the hotspots most heavily affected by human activity, it has 13 000 endemic plants, and is home to a number of interesting vertebrates such as the Spanish ibex.

   4 **Madagascar and Indian Ocean islands**
   Madagascar is a top conservation priority as this 'mini-continent' has undergone extensive deforestation. This hotspot is famous for reptiles such as chameleons and is home to all the world's lemur species.

   5 **Indo-Burma**
   An area stretching from the eastern slopes of the Himalayas through Burma and Thailand to Indochina. This region hosts the world's highest freshwater turtle diversity (43 species), and a diverse array of mammals. Several new ungulate species, such as the saola and giant muntjac, were recently discovered here.

   6 **Caribbean**
   One of the highest concentrations of species per unit area on Earth. Reptiles are particularly diverse (497 species are found here), 80 percent of which are found nowhere else. Non-fish vertebrates number 1518.

   7 **Atlantic Forest region**
   Once covering an area nearly three times the size of California, the Atlantic Forest has been reduced to about 7% of its original extent. It is most famous for 25 different kinds of primates, 20 of which are endemic. Among its best-known 'flagship species' are the critically endangered muriquis and lion tamarins.

   8 **Philippines**
   The most devastated of the hotspots, the forest cover has been reduced to 3% of its original extent. The Philippines is especially rich in endemic mammals and birds, such as the Philippine eagle.

   9 **Cape Floristic Province**
   This Mediterranean-type hotspot in southern Africa covers an area roughly the size of Ireland, and is now approximately 20% of its original extent. It is home to 8200 plant species, more than 5500 of which are endemic.

   10 **Mesoamerica**
   Forming a land bridge between two American continents, this hotspot features species representative of North and South America as well as its own unique biota. The spider and howler monkeys, Baird's tapir and unusual horned guan are 'flagship species'.

   11 **Brazilian Cerrado**
   A vast area of savanna and dry forest, the Cerrado is Brazil's new agricultural frontier and has been greatly altered by human activity in the past few decades. Home to 4400 endemic plants and several well-known mammal species, including the giant anteater, Brazilian tapir, and maned wolf.

   12 **Southwest Australia**
   A Mediterranean-type system, this hotspot is rich in endemic plants, reptiles, and marsupials including the numbat, the honey possum and quokka. It is also home to some of the world's tallest trees, e.g. the giant eucalyptus.

   13 **Mountains of South-Central China**
   An area of extreme topography, these mountains are home to several of the world's best-known mammals, including the giant panda, the red panda, and the golden monkey. This hotspot is largely unexplored and may hold many undiscovered species.

   14 **Polynesia/Micronesia**
   This hotspot comprises thousands of tiny islands scattered over the vast Pacific, from Fiji and Hawaii to Easter Island and is noteworthy for its land snails, birds, and reptiles. Hawaii has suffered some of the most severe extinctions in modern history, due in part to the introduction of non-native plant and animal species.

   15 **New Caledonia**
   One of the smallest hotspots yet it has the largest concentration of unique plants with five plant families found nowhere else on Earth. This hotspot also features many endemic birds, such as the kagu, a long-legged, flightless forest dweller representing an entire bird family.

   16 **Choco-Darien Western Ecuador**
   Some of the world's wettest rain forests are found here, and amphibians, plants and birds are particularly abundant. It has one of the highest levels of endemism of any hotspot with 210 endemic amphibian species of the 350 species found here.

   17 **Guinean Forests of West Africa** (in error, this hotspot was not numbered on the map). With the highest mammalian diversity of any hotspot, these

forests are home to the rare pygmy hippopotamus and many other striking species, including the western chimpanzee, Diana monkey and several forest duikers. The numbers of these endemic mammals have been severely reduced by large-scale logging and hunting.

18 **Western Ghats/Sri Lanka**
The Western Ghats mountain chain and adjacent island of Sri Lanka harbour high concentrations of endemic reptiles; of 259 reptile species, 161 are found nowhere else on Earth. This hotspot is also home to a number of 'flagship species', including the lion-tailed macaque.

19 **California Floristic Province**
Extending along the coast of California and into Oregon and northwestern Baja California, Mexico, this is one of five hotspots featuring a Mediterranean-type climate of hot, dry summers and cool, wet winters. It is especially rich in plants, with more than 4000 plant species, almost half of which are endemic.

20 **Succulent Karoo**
The only arid hotspot, the Succulent Karoo of southern Africa is renowned for unique succulent plants, as well as lizards and tortoises. In Namaqualand, in the southern part of this hotspot, a seasonal burst of bloom in September attracts many tourists.

21 **New Zealand**
This hotspot claims a number of world-famous endemic bird species, including kiwi (a nocturnal, flightless bird), takahe (a diurnal, flightless bird), and the critically endangered kakapo (a large, flightless parrot).

22 **Central Chile**
This hotspot features an arid region as well as a more typical Mediterranean-type zone. Best known for its incredible variety of plant species but also features unusual fauna, including one of the largest birds in the Americas, the Andean condor.

23 **Caucasus**
Situated between the Black Sea and the Caspian Sea, Caucasus habitats range from temperate forests to grasslands. A diversity of plants have been recorded here with some 6300 species, more than 1600 of which are endemic.

24 **Wallacea**
Named for the 19th century naturalist Alfred Russel Wallace, this hotspot comprises the large Indonesian island of Sulawesi, the Moluccas and many smaller islands. The area is particularly rich in endemic mammals and birds.

25 **Eastern Arc Mountains/ Coastal Forests of Tanzania and Kenya**
A chain of upland and coastal forests, this hotspot claims one of the densest concentrations of endemic plant and primate species in the world. It is home to African violets and 4000 other plant species, as well as the 1500 remaining Kirk's red colobus monkeys.

Global Warming (page 357)
1. (a) Carbon dioxide: 37.1% increase
   (b) Methane: 156.6% increase
   (c) Nitrous oxide: 18.7% increase

2. More frequent and prolonged seasonal flooding as well as permanent inundation of land. Increased coastal and inland erosion. Loss of small, low-lying atolls.

3. Increased levels of carbon dioxide, methane, and nitrous oxides act as additional blankets around the Earth, allowing the sun's energy to reach the Earth's surface, but preventing the heat escaping. This means that the Earth slowly heats up. **Note**: The atmospheric concentrations of these gases have increased dramatically above pre-industrial levels since 1750. These levels are considerably higher than at any time during the last 650,000 years (the period for which reliable data has been extracted from ice cores) and are correlated with a rise in global temperature and documented sea level rises. While correlation does not mean cause and effect, the majority of climate scientists accept the theory that the increase in anthropogenic greenhouse gas emissions is causing the rise in the Earth's temperature.

Models of Climate Change (page 359)
1. Climate change predictions involve many complicated parameters and will never be fully accurate because they are based on scenarios in which parameters can only ever be estimated. Some parameters are simplified or ignored in order to make the models workable. It is also difficult to predict future human actions, and the effect of these actions on climate change. Therefore, scientists can only suggest a likely course of events; they can not provide a definite outcome.

Ice Sheet Melting (page 360)
1. Both low sea-ice albedo and area cause more heat to be absorbed by the land and sea. This heat causes the oceans water to warm during the summer and therefore take longer to cool during the autumn (fall). This leads to winter sea-ice taking longer to form and being thinner than usual in the winter. Thin sea-ice has a lower albedo than thick sea-ice and melts faster in the spring leading to even less sea-ice the following winter. Thus thin ice and small area cover causes even thinner and less cover the following year in a potentially perpetual cycle until the sea-ice is lost.

2. Polar animals that live out on the sea-ice will be directly affected as the area covered by sea-ice reduces. Polar bears which hunt out on the ice find it harder to find food and must swim longer distances to firm ice. The reduction of sea-ice cover may also have effects on species that live below the ice as more light and heat will penetrate the waters and to deeper depths.

Global Warming and Agriculture (page 361)
1. Some crops (e.g. wheat, rice and soybeans) may benefit the higher temperatures and CO_2 levels. They may have longer growing seasons, or their growing region may expand. Other crops may be harmed by global warming. These include crops that are already being grown near their climate thresholds.

2. Climate change may allow pest species to expand their habitable range so that a wider variety of crops, or crops in previously unaffected areas, may be damaged by the pest.

Temperature and Enzyme Activity (page 362)

1. All enzymes have an optimum temperature range at which they work best. An increase in environmental temperature may put a poikilothermic organism (and its enzymes) outside its optimal range. Enzyme activity may be reduced to suboptimal levels as a result.

2. Enzymes are usually part of complicated metabolic pathways and their activity relies on substrate availability and the action of other enzymes or cofactors as well. In addition, there are unknown variables; enzymes studied in isolation often react differently to enzymes within an organism or whole system, where there may be buffers against change.

Temperature and Distribution of Species
(page 363)

1. Species distribution of *Rana* is closely related to water temperature (mating and embryonic development for each species occurs within a certain temperature range). Increasing global temperatures may result in a northwards shift of some species as their preferred water temperature shifts. Those frogs that are furthest north (*R. sylvatica*) may end up with a reduced range, while those further south (*R. clamitans*) may increase their range, depending on available habitat.

2. (a) Increased temperature speeds up the development rate in both species but, in *C.dubia*, development rates are always faster at any given temperature.
   (b) The ability of *C. dubia* to develop faster at lower temperatures gives it a competitive advantage over *C. pulchella*. *C. dubia* populations can expand early in the season without competition from *C.pulchella*, whose developmental rates lag behind at lower temperatures.

3. (a) Time to first reproduction decreases with increasing temperature. At 13°C there is a 1.5 day advantage to *C. dubia*, which reaches maturity much earlier, but at 23°C this advantage is much less.
   (b) Egg development time decreases for both species as temperature increases. However, *C. dubia* develops faster than *C. pulchella* at all temperatures presented in this study. *C. dubia* has a significant advantage at temperatures <15°C.
   (c) A temperature increase would reduce the competitive advantage of *C. dubia* over *C. pulchella* (namely earlier reproduction, development, and population establishment). The two species are likely to be competing for the same resources (small edible algae) at the same time, so both populations may be adversely affected.

4. Polar bears are forced to swim longer distances to obtain prey, and to return to the mainland for birthing. The ice sheet becomes thinner earlier in the season, and will not support their weight, so they must return to the mainland earlier. As a result, they have fewer energy reserves to get them through winter, reproductive rates are lower, as are juvenile survival rates. Their population is in decline.

Biodiversity and Global Warming (page 365)

1. Global warming will result in an increased frequency of weather extremes (floods, droughts etc) and a loss of land as coastal areas are inundated. Erosion rates may also increase as a result. Glacial retreats will reduce water supplies and snow lines will increase in altitude. Climate changes may shift the governing physical environment in certain regions (and consequently cause a shift in predominant vegetation). Ocean pH will also fall as a result of CO_2 absorption (again, with consequent changes in biotic communities).

2. (a) In general, crop growing ranges may shrink, expand, or shift. Crop plants may be affected more by higher night temperatures than by higher daytime temperatures. High night temperatures affect the ability of some crop plants such as rice to set seed and fruit. This will cause a reduction in the harvest, and a decrease in the amount of seed available for subsequent plantings.
   (b) Farmers may adjust by planting different crops in some areas, e.g. crops that are able to grow and set seed in the higher temperatures. New strains of crop plants may be able to be developed for the higher temperatures.

3. Evidence suggests that insect populations will be affected by global warming. Butterfly populations in many areas have been recorded as shifting to higher latitudes and altitudes. Fossils of insect browse damage also suggest insect populations will increase in size as temperatures rise.

4. (a) Migratory birds in the northern hemisphere are now not travelling as far south during the winter months (as higher latitudes become more hospitable) and they are making their migrations north up to two weeks earlier than usual.
   (b) Migratory birds may arrive at feeding grounds before the main food supply is ready. Plants with daylength-dependent flowering may not yet be flowering and, as a consequence, insects (and seeds and fruits) may not be in the abundance required to feed the migrants. In addition, the distribution of food resources may remain the same, but the birds are not migrating as far south and may be disconnected from their winter food supplies.

5. As air temperatures rise, so too does the snow line in alpine areas. Animals living on or above the snow line will be forced into smaller areas. If they are unable to move to higher latitudes where the snow line is lower, it is inevitable that they will become extinct in their native ranges as they run out of food and space.

Ocean Acidification (page 367)

1. D   2. C   3. B   4. A

2. pH and acidity are inversely correlated. As the pH decreases, the acidity increases.

Tropical Deforestation (page 368)

1. (a) They enhance removal of carbon dioxide from the atmosphere (anti-greenhouse).
   (b) They maintain species diversity.
   (c) They have, as-yet-undiscovered, potentially useful species for medicines etc.

2. (a-c in any order): Tropical deforestation has three primary causes: logging, fires, and road-building (associated with clearance for agriculture). Logging and fires destroy forest. Intrusion of roads into pristine

forested areas allows the invasion of weed species, increases erosion, and prevents the reestablishment of forest species. Agriculture maintains cleared areas and prevents forest reestablishment. Continued agriculture on thin tropical soils precludes the easy reestablishment of forest once the agricultural land has been abandoned.

The Impact of Introduced Species (page 369)

1. Student's own choice. Examples could include Kudzu, a deliberately introduced climbing vine that has aggressively invaded the southern US, or the red imported fire ant which were accidently introduced into the US and now how displaced native ant populations in 14 states.

2. Introduced species often have no natural controls within the new environment (e.g. no predators or natural competitors to keep their numbers in check). This means that they are able to rapidly reproduce and expand into the new area, often out-competing native or existing organisms as they do so.

Responses to Environmental Change (page 370)

1. Genetic diversity refers to the variety of alleles and genotypes present within a population.

2. (a) Low population numbers for the Illinois prairie chicken meant that there was a high degree of inbreeding between individuals. As a result, fertility rates (and production of viable offspring) decreased. This further decreased population numbers, making the inbreeding problem worse.
   (b) Introducing 271 birds into the Illinois population increased genetic diversity and increased genetic fitness of the population (more viable offspring were produced, so population numbers increased).

3. (a) At the time, farmers tended to plant only one potato variety, these meant that there was little genetic diversity between potato crops grown throughout Ireland. As a result, the majority of crops had no resistance to the fungal disease, and failed.
   (b) Tasmanian devil numbers are very low, and there is little genetic diversity within their population for the MHC gene. The predominant MHC gene within the populations cannot detect the facial cancer, so it grows unchecked. The cancer is also highly infectious, and easily spread between individuals.

4. (a) The mutation reduces the number of CCR5 receptors on T-cells. In people with the mutation in one allele, HIV infection of T-cells is slowed. Where a person has mutations in both alleles, HIV infection can not occur (person has resistance).
   (b) Caucasians in some regions of northern Europe.
   (c) People susceptible to HIV/AIDS would eventually die, leaving a higher proportion of the population with the CCR5Δ32 mutation. Eventually only those with HIV resistance would be left in the population, and the virus may no longer be able to spread. However, this is an unlikely scenario as it would take too long to occur due to the large size of the human population and our slow reproductive rate).

5. With reduced genetic diversity, there are a lmited

number of traits represented in the population. Negative selection for a particular trait will have detrimental effects on the population as a whole if there are few (or no) alternative traits. Populations with increased genetic diversity have greater capacity to resist environmental change. Some individuals will have poor fitness in a particular selective environment, but others will have alleles (and allele combinations) that provide higher fitness and will thrive.

Extinction or Evolution? (page 372)

1. (a) Adaptation by evolution is the result of changes to a population's gene pool. These changes are the result of natural selection (and genetic drift). Phenotypic plasticity causes alteration in phenotype in response to environmental change, but there are no changes to the gene pool.
   (b) Adjustment to the environment involves changes within individuals that are within the phenotypic range of the organism and may happen relatively quickly. Adaptive changes involve changes to the gene pool and take place over many generations.

2. Some species have a narrower physiological tolerance range and/or more limited phenotypic plasticity than others. These species will have limited capacity to tolerate change or make the phenotypic adjustments necessary to survive. For immobile organisms (e.g. plants), the risk may be greater because they cannot move to another location. It their offspring/seeds cannot be spread to a more favorable environment, and the individuals cannot survive and propagate where they are, then extinction is more likely.

KEY TERMS: Word Find (page 373)

```
H C X J P Y R D K S U C C E S S I O N S G A R X N
O S F E C O S Y S T E M S T A B I L I T Y W B L K
J K C O N S E R V A T I O N I K G W J X F Y X N D
O P Z E A Z W D I S T R I B U T I O N S X J D I V
G E C O L O G I C A L S U C C E S S I O N G F K S
R E V S E C O N D A R Y S U C C E S S I O N M B I
E V T P N B U J L N K E Y S T O N E S P E C I E S
E D W M G C G R N L P O L L U T I O N G S V T K K
N O K P R I M A R Y S U C C E S S I O N E I U K E
H M P M D E N D A N G E R E D S P E C I E S G N V
O H I N T R O D U C E D B A B U N D A N C E N H O
U G R E E A A S H C L I M A T E C H A N G E L L O
S K Q D G E H Z T W W B P B I O D I V E R S I T Y
E T T H R E A T E N E D S P E C I E S E D B H P S
G U R B A N I Z A T I O N J I H V L S E G K J W L
A X F L I E G L O B A L W A R M I N G U X N T T T
S G H I O B F D X G R E E N H O U S E E F F E C T
```

Answer list below given in the same order as the clues in the student workbook: biodiversity, conservation, ecosystem stability, endangered species, global warming, greenhouse effect, greenhouse gas, pollution, primary succession, secondary succession, ecological succession, urbanization, distribution, succession, threatened species, abundance, keystone species, introduced, climate change.